Western Land and Water Use

Western
Land and Water Use

By Mont H. Saunderson

NORMAN

UNIVERSITY OF OKLAHOMA PRESS

Preface

Dᴜʀɪɴɢ the past twenty years, I have worked with several national and regional administrative and scientific agencies in the development of Western land- and water-use policies and programs. In 1947 I served with the American Farm Bureau Federation, and especially with the Land and Water Use Committee of that organization. During these past two decades, much new information has been developed concerning Western resource use, new concepts have evolved, and much debate has occurred about those public policies affecting Western land and water use.

It is my purpose, in the following pages, to bring this information, these concepts, and these arguments into focus as objectively as possible. Wide comprehension of these materials and of their significance is very important to the future course of Western development. Some of the data presented here are national rather than regional, and are included as background for the distinctly Western materials.

Some of these materials extend into a twilight zone, where facts are not yet fully developed, and where wisdom is yet immature. Conclusions drawn concerning such materials are, consequently, partly in the realm of belief and are controversial. It is perhaps inevitable that those conclusions may be somewhat colored by the author's beliefs and philosophy. In this work I have used many sources, especially those of the Western land-grant colleges, the United States Department of Agriculture, and the United States Department of the Interior.

This presentation must be regarded as my own responsibility; it is not offered in any official capacity. I was on leave

v

from my work in the United States Forest Service during the preparation of this book.

Among the many who have aided me in the preparation of this work, I wish especially to acknowledge the valuable help of Mr. Joseph Ackerman, associate director of the Farm Foundation.

The materials of this publication were reviewed by the Committee on Tenure, Credit, and Land Values of the Northern Great Plains Agricultural Advisory Council. This committee recommends publication of these materials, believing that such publication will serve a valuable purpose. Conclusions drawn and views given are, it is understood, those of the author.

MONT H. SAUNDERSON

Denver, Colorado
March 18, 1950

Contents

Illustrations

Western Land and Water Use

I. Western Land Resources and the National Economy

A Gaze into the Crystal

Recent studies of our national population trends indicate that we probably shall reach a population total of 163,000,000 some twenty-five years hence, or in 1975, and that the figure may be 185,000,000. What does this portend in terms of our agricultural production and needed acreage of agricultural cropland?

As we do our "crystal gazing" to discover the answer, let us think of two possibilities of agricultural demand for a population of 163,000,000 people. One of these assumes a high—but realistic and attainable—level of industrial activity, employment, and income; the other, a moderate level of activity and income. To translate the first of these postulates into terms of food consumption, let us use as a standard the annual food consumption of those families in the United States who in 1941 had an income above two thousand dollars—a group comprising about 40 per cent of the total population. For the second or moderate-income postulate, let us take as a standard the annual per capita average of food consumption in the United States during the years 1937–41.

Then, assuming that the level of income is high, the per capita consumption in 1975 would be 190 pounds of meat, 925 pounds of milk and milk products, 219 pounds of wheat, and 168 pounds of vegetables. To attain these levels of meat and milk production for a population of 163,000,000 people, we should have to maintain 94,000,000 head of all cattle, 31,000,000 milch cows, 65,000,000 sheep, and 15,800,000 brood sows.

If the level of income is only moderate in 1975, the comparable figures would be 155 pounds of meat, 810 pounds of milk

3

and milk products, 218 pounds of wheat, and 130 pounds of vegetables. Meat and milk production at this level would call for 82,000,000 head of all cattle, 27,000,000 milch cows, 56,500,000 sheep, and 13,500,000 brood sows.

Now into our crystal must come the imagery of our agricultural technology—of the possible future progress in our biology, chemistry, and mechanics. During the 1937–41 period we had in use some 412,000,000 acres of cropland, or an average of just about three acres per capita. We anticipate some acceleration in the rate of improvement due to the application of science, and the amount of cropland that we shall need in 1975 will depend in part upon what happens to the per acre production of the land. We foresee a continued uptrend in that production equal at least to the uptrend of the 1930–40 decade.

In the clearing field of our crystal we see the figure 416,000,-000. This is the figure of cropland acreage that we shall need in 1975 to fill our food and fiber needs under the high income level. This figure of 416,000,000 comes out at about two and one-half acres per capita. The figure for the moderate income level, using the same set of assumptions as to trends in our agricultural technology, is 366,000,000, or two and one-fourth acres per capita. Compare these acreage totals with our 1946 figure of 413,000,000 acres of cropland used.

But there is one section of the crystal's field that remains cloudy and obscure. That is the part where we look for answers concerning the effects of soil erosion and depletion upon croplands, crop yield, and cropland acreage requirements. Probably we are now destroying croplands, as far as their future agricultural use is concerned, at a rate of one-half million acres to one million acres each year.

Equally important, perhaps more so, is the fact that soil erosion and depletion now bring an unknown acreage of cropland down toward the economic margin in their competition with the better lands. That question and the related questions of the influence of prices and land-use margins upon the use of depleted

4

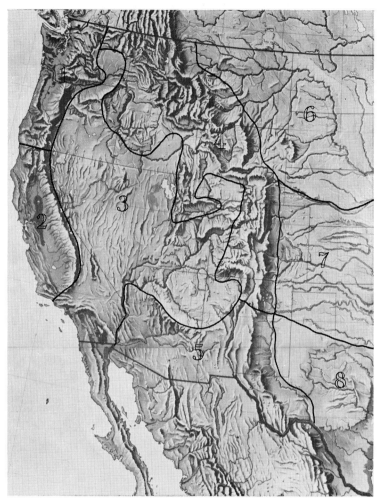

Land-use regions in the Western United States

1 Pacific Northwest	5 Southwest
2 California	6 Northern Plains
3 Intermountain	7 Central Plains
4 Rocky Mountain	8 Southern Plains

lands make the outcome uncertain. But, apparently, if we can conquer the ogre of land destruction, we shall see near miracles of agricultural production from the nation's good croplands. And we can, presumably, maintain an animal population far above that of the past, with the increase maintained largely or wholly from the production of the croplands.

We can increase our Western croplands through irrigation reclamation by ten to twenty million acres. We can increase our croplands of the central West and the South through drainage reclamation by twenty-five to fifty million acres. That is a total of thirty-five to sixty million possible new acres of croplands. We may need them.

WESTERN IRRIGATION

ALTHOUGH crops raised on irrigated lands represent only 9 or 10 per cent of the total value of all farm products in the United States, the importance of certain crops that are produced by irrigation is impressive. Irrigation farming produces about three-fourths of the sugar beets, one-third of the alfalfa hay, and one-fourth of the potatoes produced in the United States. Approximately one-fourth of the nation's total orchard acreage is irrigated, and a high proportion of our winter vegetable production comes from irrigated farms in California and Arizona. Some specialty crops, raisins for example, are produced entirely on irrigated farms.

Some twenty to twenty-four million acres of land are irrigated in the seventeen Western states.[1] Probably there are about twenty million acres in what can truly be termed irrigation farming. The other two to four million acres are under partial and low-intensity irrigation. Much of this is stock-ranch irriga-

[1] These include the eleven states lying wholly in the West (Arizona, California, Colorado, Idaho, Montana, Nevada, New Mexico, Oregon, Utah, Washington, and Wyoming) and the states of the Great Plains area (North and South Dakota, Nebraska, Kansas, Oklahoma, and Texas) lying partially in what is considered here as the West.

tion and meadowland and forage crops, where low-cost diversions of small streams or of spring runoff waters are used for a single irrigation. The large acreages of dry-land crops in the plains states cut the proportion of irrigated land in the West to 10 per cent of the total cropland acreage of the seventeen Western states.

In the eleven states west of the Great Plains—states which contain most of the irrigated lands of the United States—the irrigated acreage is near 30 per cent of the total cropland acreage. Irrigated agriculture produces over half of the total agricultural income of these eleven states.[2] Beyond this actual cash value, the production of the irrigated farm areas is important because the stability of the other segments of the Western agricultural economy in a large measure depends upon it. Especially is this true of the near-by range livestock operations, which may buy hay and pasturage in the irrigated areas to fill in the seasonal gaps of the range-land grazing.

Total Western irrigation acreage and the distribution of this acreage are shown in the table below.

Irrigated Lands in the Western States

(Acreage actually irrigated in 1939, as shown by the 1940 census)

State	Acreage	State	Acreage
Arizona	653,263	Oklahoma	4,160
California	5,069,568	Oregon	1,049,176
Colorado	3,220,685	South Dakota	60,198
Idaho	2,277,857	Texas	1,045,224
Kansas	99,980	Utah	1,176,116
Montana	1,711,409	Washington	615,013
Nebraska	610,379	Wyoming	1,486,498
Nevada	739,863		
New Mexico	554,039		
North Dakota	21,615	Total	20,395,043

[2] This statement is based upon agricultural census data showing the total cash farm income of these states and the part of that income from irrigated crops and from livestock and livestock products produced with the aid of irrigated crops and pastures.

Approximately 40 per cent of this total acreage of irrigation was developed under individual and partnership enterprise, and another 40 per cent as co-operative enterprise. Federal government reclamation accounts for only two million out of the twenty million, although the federal reclamation developments also furnish some supplemental water to another two million acres of the eighteen million acres of private enterprise irrigation.

Most of the present and the planned expansion of Western irrigation is now on federal reclamation projects. These are, in the main, large and multipurpose projects. Investment in their irrigation development, though important, is less than the investment in power, flood control, and navigation. Power development is definitely the chief purpose of some of these projects.

Private enterprise irrigation has in the past constructed most of the irrigation feasible at low cost and without large capital sources and subsidies for public-value features. Probably most of the future development of Western irrigation will come through federal reclamation projects. Some ten million acres of land will be served by such projects now under construction or authorized for construction. Nearly half of this development is for supplemental water to lands now irrigated. It is estimated that Western water resources are sufficient for an ultimate development of some forty million acres of irrigation, or about double the present acreage.

Federal reclamation was originally conceived to prepare the public domain lands for homesteading. Such developments of these lands as were feasible have now been largely accomplished, and present federal reclamation projects concern primarily lands now in private ownership, either as unirrigated land or as partially developed irrigation.

One such project is the Missouri basin development which is now under way. An ultimate of 5,000,000 acres may be brought under irrigation as a result of this development. This is privately owned land; some 500,000 acres of it is land now irrigated. The acreage to be irrigated under the Columbia River Grand Coulee project totals approximately 1,029,000 acres. This is all nonirrigated land, of which some 979,000 acres is privately owned. The Colorado–Big Thompson project will furnish supplemental water to about 615,000 acres of land now in private irrigation developments. Upon completion of the proposed federal reclamation program in the California Central Valley, some 550,000 acres of privately owned land would be brought under new irrigation. This mammoth project would also provide water for some 1,350,-000 acres of presently irrigated land that now lacks adequate surface water or that is exhausting the ground-water resources. Some of the San Joaquin Valley pump irrigation now draws water from a depth of 700 feet. The proposed Central Arizona Project, if undertaken, would provide water mainly for the 600,-000 acres of presently irrigated land in the Gila River drainage. Without it, this acreage will likely be severely reduced.

We shall certainly see an expansion of Western irrigation as a feature of continued Western growth and development. In time this development will be needed to take care of the national and Western population increases and the necessary retirement of land on which farming is becoming unprofitable because of erosion and land deterioration. This development should, however, be properly meshed with our whole agricultural economy, and the lands to which the available water resources will be applied must be selected with care.

CALIFORNIA, HERE WE COME!

SINCE 1940 and the rise of West Coast war industry, an ever increasing tide of migration has been pouring into the Pacific Coast states from all over the nation. Population analysts say that were this migration trend of the past several years to continue, the entire population of the United States would be located in these three westernmost states within seventy years.

This rate of migration cannot, of course, be sustained. For the recent rate of population shift must eventually be matched by a shift in industrial capacity and jobs. We are witnessing some of that, too, though we lack any good measurement of just how much. But in the recent rapid growth of the cities of the Pacific states, we see an unmistakable trend—a shifting of population that will, to a considerable extent, cause a correlated relocation of industrial capacity.

Those who are studying the nation's trends of population and migration hazard a guess that by 1975 the population of the West Coast states will have increased by two-thirds above the 1940 figure (already this guess looks very conservative), while during this same period the national increase will be about one-fifth. And the population of the Rocky Mountain and Intermountain states of the West will, they believe, increase at about the same rate as the national total.

Let us try to envision what this population trend may signify to Western land use and land policy. First, for California this great and continuing increase means an urgent need for well-planned development, conservation, and use of the water and power resources of the Central Valley. The same applies to Colorado River water and power for Southern California. The Central Valley district probably has adequate water for its ultimate development, but the use of that water will depend upon gigantic engineering works to transport the surplus waters of the Sacramento River to the lands and the cities of the San Joaquin Valley.

Plans for these works are now developed, and the Federal Bureau of Reclamation has embarked upon the engineering program. But the program may be slowed or stymied by the present crosscurrents of economic interests and conflicts of ideologies. Public versus private hydroelectric power, federal control over the water resources of multipurpose reservoirs, and the application of the 160-acre farm limitation where Federal reclamation development by public funds brings high value increments to private landowners—these are the issues back of the conflicts.

For Southern California the future may require a complete

overhauling of the present Colorado River Interstate Water Compact. This compact divided the waters of the Colorado equally between the upper-basin and the lower-basin states. Then in order to reach an agreement with the other lower-basin states —Arizona and Nevada—for the authorization of Hoover Dam, California enacted legislation limiting her own share of the Colorado River water to 4,400,000 acre-feet out of the lower basin's annual total of 7,500,000 acre-feet.

But the Southern California planners who foresee a water and power shortage for Southern California people, lands, and industries now look askance at the California allotment in the Colorado River Interstate Water Compact.

The growth of population, cities, and industries in the West Coast states signifies certain changes in land use and economics for the other Western states beyond their borders. For markets, these other Western states are going to look more to the West, less to the East. California now consumes twice the amount of beef that is produced within the state's borders. Beef cattle now move west from the pastures and feed lots of the Rocky Mountain states, whereas ten years ago these shipments moved to St. Paul, Omaha, and Kansas City. Beef production in these Western states already feels the incentive to increase the amount and the quality of pasture and feed-lot finishing of animals for the West Coast markets.

This influence of the West Coast markets upon the agriculture of the other Western states, as exemplified by Western beef production and consumption, may cause a considerable recasting of the economics of Western irrigation expansion, favorable to such expansion.

Meanwhile, migration, apparently inevitable and inexorable, continues westward. It is one of the many of our nation's burgeonings. It will mean local, regional, and national economic adjustments, which we should try to foresee, and with which both our individual planning and our national policy making must reckon.

WESTERN WATER RESOURCES

WITH THE GROWTH of population in the Western states and the expansion of irrigation and of industrial uses of water, full use of Western water resources is now foreseen. What are these resources, and how may they limit Western growth and development?

As one measure of these water resources we may use the water-yield estimates of the Western national forests—the watershed lands that yield most of the water available for use in the eleven Western states. These estimates are given below for the six Forest Service regions in the West. Stream gage records from nineteen Western national forests constitute the sample on which these estimates are based. This measure of water yield from the Western national forest watersheds does not constitute the total annual water resource of the eleven Western states, but probably does account for most of the water yield.

Water Yield of the National Forests of the United States West of the 101st Meridian

Region	Runoff in acre-feet per year	Acreage in the National Forest Watershed	Acre-feet per acre
1. All of Montana, north Idaho, northeast Washington	24,300,000	24,300,000	1.0
2. All of Colorado, Wyoming east of the Continental Divide	14,000,000	19,690,000	0.7
3. All of New Mexico and Arizona	6,000,000	20,450,000	0.3
4. All of Utah and Nevada, Idaho south of the Salmon, Wyoming west of the Divide	24,500,000	30,640,000	0.8
5. All of California	20,500,000	18,650,000	1.1
6. All of Oregon, Washington except northeast	58,200,000	23,280,000	2.5

This regional picture of Western water resources tells a story.

A surprising amount of this resource is in the Pacific Northwest. Oregon and Washington have, and long will have, ample water. We see why the water-starved Southwest wishes to tap Colorado River water sources. California has a large water resource, but much of this is in the northern or Sacramento River part of the Central Valley. California growth and development, as now foreseen, will require all of the water resources of the Central Valley and all of or more than the allotment of Colorado River water under the Colorado River Compact. Should the present plans for an ultimate total of forty million acres of Western irrigation be realized, such irrigation would require considerably more than half of the total Western water resources.

Irrigation development has already overreached the available water supply in a number of locations. One instance of this is in the Gila Basin of Arizona, where surface water and pumped ground water will not serve the present irrigated acreage. The proposed Central Arizona Project would, at great cost, bring Colorado River water to the irrigated areas in the Gila Basin. Other instances of expansion of agriculture beyond water resources may be seen in parts of the San Joaquin Valley of California, where pump irrigation has for years made an overdraft on the ground-water resources.

Ground-water resources, more and more widely used as the sole source of irrigation water or as a supplement to surface water, may or may not be a part of the annual water-yield resource. In some situations the ground-water recharge comes quickly from surface water, but in other locations the ground water is not a renewable resource. In this latter case the ground water is of geologic character, slowly trapped in deep ground storage over thousands of years. Where extensive irrigation use has been made of this type of water resource, the resource is being slowly exhausted. A lift of several hundred feet is now necessary in some such irrigation, and the end is near unless feasible means can be found for recharge of the ground waters by surface waters.

12

In the coming competition for the Western water resources, the present annual yield of the watersheds is probably about the only resource to be had. Competition will have to center around the storage, conservation, and transportation—within the economic limits—of the present resource. It is unlikely that cloud nucleation—"seeding" of clouds from airplanes—can add appreciably to the Western water resource. Any appreciable precipitation usually results from contact of two air masses over some period of time, not by a change occurring within one air mass.

It is possible that management of the upland watershed lands can increase their water yield, yet keep the mountain soils intact. This and other features of the Western water resources will in time be explored, for the need of this resource will become acute, the competition for it, intense.

OASIS AT THE FOOT OF THE WASATCH

PHYSIOGRAPHY, that branch of geology dealing with the geography of the physical features of the earth, recognizes three main divisions of the Rocky Mountains.

The Northern Rockies end with the Beartooth Plateau, where the spectacular Cook City highway enters Yellowstone Park. Then, beginning with the Shoshone Range, east of Yellowstone Park, the Middle Rockies reach into central Utah, ending at Mount Nebo. South from Nebo the Utah Mountains are part of the plateaus of the Colorado River drainage. Finally, the Southern Rockies reach from near Laramie, Wyoming, south to Santa Fé, New Mexico, completing the Rocky Mountain system.

Let us turn our attention to the Central Rocky Mountains, and then, more locally, to that part of the Central Rockies known as the Wasatch Mountains. These mountains constitute the southern part of the Central Rockies; they reach from Mount Nebo in Central Utah to the Wellsville Range west of Cache Valley in northern Utah. This mountainous spine of northern Utah reaches an elevation of nearly twelve thousand feet at Timpanogos Peak, near Provo.

13

In the Wasatch is one of the most intensive and complex uses of mountain lands in the West. As a consequence some of the most important land management problems arise from the use of such lands. For here are densely peopled rural communities and growing cities that look to the mountains for water, for livestock grazing, and for recreation—camping, summer homes, hunting, and fishing. Let us view the watershed features of these mountains first.

As the Pacific air masses push across the Sierras and the Cascades, those that move toward the Central Rockies do not encounter any high mountains until they reach the Central Rockies. With some minor exceptions, like the Rubies of northeastern Nevada and the Steens of southeastern Oregon, the mountains of the Great Basin may be classed as desert mountains.

But the Wasatch are sufficient in elevation, mass, and length to wring the moisture from the Pacific air masses. These are not desert mountains; they have abundant vegetation and deep, dark soil in their upper reaches. Precipitation records indicate that the average annual precipitation rises to 30 or 40 inches at the ten-thousand-foot level of these mountains. Snow surveys show winter snow accumulations of 150 inches, containing up to 25 inches of water, in the highest elevations of the Wasatch.

These mountains are truly humid oases in a desert, however. Forty miles west of their crest the average annual precipitation drops to about 6 inches. To the east, the average annual precipitation decreases to 6.24 inches at Green River, Utah. Locally, the lands to the east and the west of the Wasatch are spoken of as the "West Desert" and the "East Desert." From atop the Wasatch Range on a clear summer day, one can see, though not feel, the furnacelike heat of the arid lands.

Along the steep west-facing front of the Wasatch one sees the meaning of the words "oasis at the foot of the Wasatch." For it is here that the streams of the Wasatch formed their soil deltas under prehistoric Lake Bonneville, which once rose al-

14

most one thousand feet above the present Great Salt Lake level. Now these same streams carry the water from the Wasatch watershed to the irrigation storages and canals that serve the farm lands of the ancient soil deltas that were formed when the climate was humid. On these lands and waters rural Utah has grown and developed. Here is a density of rural population comparable with that of Belgium and the Netherlands. Growing cities and industries now compete with these farms for the waters of the Wasatch.

Thus in economic terms we see the Wasatch first as a high-value watershed. At the foot of these mountains, where farms and cities cover the limited soils of Bonneville, precipitation amounts to sixteen or eighteen inches annually. This rises steadily, as the altitude increases, to forty inches or even more at some places on the crest. But not until the elevation is around six thousand feet does the precipitation balance the evaporation from the land and the transpiration of the vegetation. This is to say that there is no net balance for water runoff or yield from these mountain lands below the level of six thousand feet. Consequently, the lands above that elevation are really the watershed lands. Those above seven thousand feet yield most of the water and constitute the really valuable watershed lands.

Measurements of the water yields from these watershed lands and of the irrigation water used on the farm lands show that the average water yield from seven acres of the watershed is required for each acre of the irrigated farms. The average value per acre for these farm lands divided by the seven acres of the watershed land amounts to something over thirty dollars an acre, the "protection value" of the watershed. This value depends upon the watershed serving its purpose, but the watershed functions of these lands can be greatly changed, perhaps even destroyed. When we bring into this calculation the urban values that depend upon the waters from these mountains, this "protection value" of the water-yield lands reaches an extremely high figure. Yet we sometimes think of these mountain lands as

15

low-yield lands for timber and grazing uses, having only low per acre values for protection and management.

Studies of the watershed aspects of these lands by the United States Forest Service, the management agency for the lands of the Wasatch that are in the national forests, show that the maintenance of the upland soils and vegetation is the first requirement in watershed management. Topsoils and vegetation infiltrate the melting snow water and summer rain into the rock strata of the mountains, retarding the snow melt and the runoff. The consequence is an even flow of the water through the summer. Where soils and vegetation have been depleted and eroded as a result of overgrazing, fire, and overlogging, there is more early water—which will likely carry undesirable sediments—and less late water. And the underground storages, which those areas that use well irrigation depend upon, are deprived of some of their recharge.

Another result of injury to these watershed lands is the disastrous floods that may come off bare soils in the uplands. When the occasional intense summer storms strike on the areas of bare upland soils—some of these lands were literally grazed into "dust beds" forty years ago—an awesome, grinding flow of water, mud, and boulders may roar down one of the steep canyons. When these floods emerge from a canyon, they devastate farm lands, homes, and even villages. These farm lands, formed under Lake Bonneville, experienced no such flood before the misuse of the mountain land high up on the Wasatch.

Although the Wasatch Mountains now lie principally within the boundaries of the national forest, a great deal of this land came into private ownership as homesteads. These private lands, as well as the national forest lands, are under heavy demand for livestock grazing. Large acreages of winter range in the deserts —too great in proportion to the complementary summer range available in the Wasatch—and the needs of the heavy rural population for agricultural resources have resulted, and still result, in overgrazing of the mountain lands. Reductions in grazing use

16

necessary for the protection of watersheds in the national forests are now in progress. Towns and irrigation organizations are in some instances buying private lands within the national forests and rehabilitating them for watershed management. For here water from the mountains means life. Sufficient of the mountain soils are now gone from some of the drainages to change materially the regimen of the stream.

On a clear, frosty day in late winter, skiers can be seen flashing in the sun in the high mountain basins above Salt Lake City and Ogden. Those mountain slopes have a covering of over one hundred inches of well-settled snow. That snow is "white gold" to the farm lands and the cities of the oasis below. Watershed uses and values of these mountain lands are paramount. All other uses must, in wisdom, be adjusted to maintain the watershed values whenever the other uses conflict with the management of the mountain lands as watersheds.

Pack Rats and Haymakers

On a clear winter day we look west to the Southern Rocky Mountains from a point in the Central Plains near Greeley, Colorado. Sharp and distinct against a deep blue horizon bulk the ranges of these great uplands, rising from the place where the plains meet the first low hills at an elevation of about fifty-five hundred feet, to the alpine masses that tower above fourteen thousand feet.

We see clearly the dark band of the evergreen-forested lands occupying the elevation between six thousand and eleven thousand feet. Above the upper timber line lie the great glistening snow fields; below the lower limit of the timber the low foothills roll down to the patchwork snow cover of the plains.

These low foothills and the plains for a distance of some sixty miles eastward lie in the rain shadow of the alpine country that rears high above the buttressing lower ranges. These arid lands of the rain shadow receive only fourteen inches of moisture in a

17

year. The alpine lands receive from forty to fifty! And the lower limit of the timber zone marks the transition where tree seedlings cannot compete with grass for the limited topsoil moisture.

Just a few weeks hence and winter's snow will leave the open grasslands of the lowest foothills and begin its retreat up the mountain. First of the timber land to clear will be the elevation zone occupied by the ponderosa or Western yellow pine—from about six thousand up to nine thousand feet in the Southern Rockies. From these lands and on up to timber line the snow will then recede more slowly through the forested land zone occupied by the spruce and the fir. Finally the snow fields above timber line will give way to a flowering tundra.

From the alpine tundra to the plains grasslands we can read a story of natural uses of land. Contrasts in the animal life forms as well as in the flora of the zones tell us this story. In the alpine country next August, we shall see the "haymaker" literally "making hay while the sun shines" during the scant two months of the growing season. This diminutive bunny, the Rocky Mountain rock coney, cuts the mountain grasses and spreads them to dry. Then he stores them in his underground caverns for food during the eight months when the snow lies deep over his abode. Locally he is known as the "haymaker."

These alpine lands afford lush grazing for the range sheepman's ewe and lamb bands for a period of about sixty days. But such use must be subordinate to the most valuable natural use of these lands—as watersheds. The soil mantle is the blotter that soaks up the melting snow and feeds the water into underground storage. In time, this water will reappear at lower outlets to supply cities and irrigate farm lands. Were that soil mantle to break and erode, the water quality and the water yield characteristics of these mountains would change greatly.

From the alpine lands we shift our gaze downward over the timber zone—past the spruce and fir and down to the ponderosa pine zone of the lower mountains. Here the lands are privately owned; those above, starting with the upper part of the pon-

18

derosa zone, are in the national forests. A closer view would reveal the bunch grasses under the open timber stands of these lower mountains and would cause us to wonder whether the natural use of these lands is grazing, timber production, or some combination of these and other uses. The answer is suggested by the presence of the pack rat. He prefers to live in the arid lands.

The growth cycle of the ponderosa pine on the dry lands runs from eighty to one hundred twenty years. Private land economy has, consequently, a strong incentive to manage these lands for an annual grazing revenue rather than for a deferred future revenue from timber. But both the timber and the grass cover have served to form and to hold the soil on these steep lands. Where the grazing use has been at all heavy, we see long erosion gashes running up what once were the grassy drainageways of the gulches. Although these lands do not yield much water, they are a primary source of the sediments that are filling the reservoirs in the plains below. We conclude that the natural use of these lands is timber production and watershed conservation and that grazing is secondary and should be limited. Private land economy has not given that result, and probably will not without public aids and controls.

From our vantage point in the plains we have looked at the picture of natural land use for the Rocky Mountain country to the west of us. We might do the same for the country that serves as our vantage point—this great body of land known as the Central Plains. From the Pine Ridge escarpment of western Nebraska they sweep to the "Break of the Plains," or the end of the Ogallala limestone cap in northern Texas. But theirs is a separate story.

Dry-Land Wheatlands

WHEAT FROM THE DRY LANDS of the West constitutes the largest item of Western food production—in value, greater than sugar beets, greater than the citrus crop, and greater than the total range livestock production. This great outpouring of bread grain during the past ten years has been a veritable bonanza for the Western wheat regions. During this time nearly three-fourths of the nation's large wheat production has come from the Western dry lands.

Although the need for such a wheat crop as that of the past decade may depend upon the future course of our international policies, the issues of policy concerning the future of this land resource seem clear. We can do with less wheat where wheat farming means rapid loss of the resource. What is this resource, in the several main wheat-producing regions of the West, and how long can the present wheatland use be maintained?

Three regions account for most of the Western wheat production. Most important of these is the Central Plains, where some thirty million acres are used in dry-land wheat farming. Next in acreage and production are the Northern Plains, with approximately twenty million acres in dry-land wheat farming. Third in importance are the three Pacific Northwest states of Washington, Idaho, and Oregon, now having a total of around six million acres of land in wheat farming. These acreages are higher than the seeded acreages, because of the summer fallowing of part of the land each year.

Central Plains wheat production is entirely from fall-sown wheat. Drought, intense March and April winds, and lack of good tillage and farming practices caused a heavy wind-erosion toll on many of these lands during the thirties. During the past ten climatically favorable years the known conservation methods and practices have not been as fully used as need be. Large acreages of land with poor soil and high erosion potential have been brought into cultivation in recent years. Much of this land was once farmed and later abandoned. Some of it is new breaking. Most of this land recently brought into re-use or new use does not have a long-time average yield capacity above the margin for a normal cost and income ratio. Sometimes this land is on

20

the fringes of the good dry-land areas. Sometimes it is in areas that, in their entirety, are just not suited for dry-land cropping.

Northern Plains wheat production comes mainly from spring-sown grain, though fall-sown wheat is important in the Shelby–Great Falls–Havre triangle of Montana and in the Montana Judith Basin and Yellowstone Valley. According to the record, Northern Plains wheat acreage has been expanded somewhat during the past decade. Much of this land has, however, a long-time yield average that will not pay the production cost in any normal cost and price relationship. This is true even when such land is farmed in large and efficiently mechanized units. Probably not much more than half of the present Northern Plains wheat acreage is really suited for sustained dry-land wheat production. The acreage that is so suited will, in the long run, yield almost as much wheat as comes from the present total acreage. Northern Plains spring wheat is, in most years, high-quality milling wheat. Because of its usually high protein content this wheat commands substantial premiums in the years when the Central Plains winter wheat crop is below standard in this feature of quality.

Areas producing most of the wheat in the Pacific Northwest are the Palouse Hills area of eastern Washington and north-western Idaho, the Big Bend area of central Washington, and the Walla Walla and Pendleton area of Washington and Oregon. Most of this wheat is fall-sown, and most of the grain is of the soft varieties that are not regarded as good bread grains. Except in the Big Bend area, the wheat yields are good and fairly dependable. All or nearly all of these lands have, however, severe erosion problems. Although the progress in meeting these has been substantial during the past fifteen years, the effort has been entirely inadequate. Here is a good wheatland resource that will rapidly become submarginal unless our conservation program work and educational work can attain much faster and better results than have been attained to the present time. During the thirties, under the federal agricultural program, the eroding

21

lands of the Palouse Hills, especially the steep slopes, were seeded to legumes. Cropping was resumed, generally, during the recent war period. Soils of these hill lands are deep and fertile, but not indestructible.

During the past few years we have had several wheat crops with a national total exceeding one billion bushels. But the climatic situation has been, in the over-all Western picture, unusually good. High yields and high wheat prices have brought fantastic incomes from the cropping of many of the wheatlands of the West. In the western Great Plains, where the dry-land agriculture is so expansible, the result of this combination of high yields and high prices seems inevitable. We are going to have a recurrence of the pains of readjustment in Western dry-land agriculture.

WESTERN RANGE LANDS AND RANCHES

WESTERN RANGE LANDS and stock ranches present a great variety of resources and ranch uses of these resources. These differences in range lands and ranch types can be characterized best in terms of the main natural regions of the West. These regions are described in Chapter III under the heading "Future Uses and Values of Western Lands." More than any other type of agricultural production, Western stock ranching must adapt to its natural environment, rather than modifying that environment by crop culture. Let us view the contrasts in range-land resources and the consequent differences in types of ranches in the several natural regions of the West.

Range lands of the Northern Plains region have one main type of range forage, known as the mixed-prairie type. In this type we see a well-balanced proportion of the mid-grasses and the short grasses. Principal of the mid-grasses is the Western wheat grass. Blue grama constitutes the main short grass. This combination of mid-grasses and short grasses affords good range forage through the eight to ten months' range season. Mixed-prairie forage, owing to the predominance of grasses and the lack

22

of browse and weed forage, makes better cattle range than sheep range. Because these are not coarse grasses, they do, however, constitute fairly good sheep forage. Winter feeds grown by the stock ranches of this region consist mainly of dry-land crops, principally small-grain hay, sweet clover, and corn. Wherever possible, the ranches have irrigated alfalfa or native grass meadows, using the spring runoff or local storage to irrigate.

Northern Plains range forage and soils have not been much changed through past use, though the use has been heavy at times. Soils are stable, and the native grasses are durable. Lowered livestock weights and impaired ranch incomes seem to follow without much lag the overuse of this range type. It is one of the few types of Western range resource to withstand bankruptcy from overuse longer than the ranch itself. Livestock numbers were drastically reduced by the 1931–38 drought period, but favorable years have restored most of this range to good condition.

Northern Plains sheep ranches raise principally fine-wool sheep, although in recent years they have been making some use of the Columbia and other whiteface crossbreeds in an attempt to increase the lamb production. Cattle ranches of this region now operate largely on a breeding-herd basis and market feeder calves to the corn-belt farms. In the future they will likely return more to the marketing of yearlings, to afford some "cushion" for possible adverse seasons.

Central Plains ranges tend more to the short-grass type, although they originally had a good complement of the mid-grasses. Apparently the cool climate mid-grasses of the Northern Plains reach their climatic limit in the Central Plains, for they disappear under grazing pressure. The loss of the mid-grasses and the predominance of the short grasses have made this range seasonally unbalanced. Now it is primarily a summer and fall range. It lacks plants suitable for spring forage and winter use. Buffalo grass and the gramas, the main short grasses of this range, grow mainly during the summer.

23

As a consequence of this change in the Central Plains range type and the extensive development of dry-land crop farming in this region, the livestock operations are stock farms rather than stock ranches. These stock farms use the short-grass range for summer and fall pasturage, fall-sown wheat for winter and spring grazing, and grain sorghums for the winter feed supplement. Stock ranches that depend mainly on the range are handicapped in operating on a year-round, or breeding-herd, basis because of the limited seasonal suitability of the range. Hence many of the cattle ranches now buy stocker cattle in the late spring for summer and fall pasturage and for sale in October or November. Cattle operations predominate over sheep operations in the Central Plains. One limiting factor for range sheep is the lack of suitable winter feeds. The coarse dry-land roughages that can be grown are better suited to cattle.

The Southern Plains can be divided into two subregions— the Edwards Plateau and the Río Grande Plain. The main range type of the Edwards Plateau is a rather complex association of browse plants, weeds, grasses, and cacti. This naturally productive range will, when in good condition, provide reasonably well-balanced year-round forage for both cattle and sheep. Originally much of the Edwards Plateau was essentially a grassland, with a good cover of the short grasses and the Southwestern desert grasses. Overstocking of these grass ranges with cattle and suppression of the range fires have caused the mesquite and other treelike shrubs to increase markedly. Now the main enterprise of the ranches is range sheep, cattle being a secondary enterprise and mohair goats sometimes a third in this combination. Sheep are usually grazed in fenced pastures, not herded in range bands.

Range lands of the Río Grande Plain have the coarser and taller grasses of a subhumid region. They are, consequently, cattle ranges. Some of these cattle ranches are very large, the King Ranch being one of the largest. Although the mesquite tree is a range problem over much of central and southern Texas, this problem is most acute in the Río Grande Plain. Dense growth of the mesquite reduces range forage and impedes management of the livestock. Where the mesquite can be controlled, these range lands have a high grazing capacity. Almost universally, the cattle ranches of the Río Grande Plain use a cross between the Brahman and one of the American beef breeds for their range animal. This cross resists the parasites, insects, diseases, and heat of this climate.

We look now across the Pecos to the range lands of the Southwest. Range lands of the Texas trans-Pecos country and of southern New Mexico may be described as desert grasslands. They are cattle ranges, almost entirely. These grasslands and their soils have suffered extensive depletion; there has been a widespread increase in the juniper and other trees and shrubs and in the cacti. Many of the ranches that once could market a good crop of feeder calves now market thin mature cattle as stockers and feeders.

Another important range area of the Southwest is the "Mexican highlands" area of southeastern Arizona and southwestern New Mexico. This is a grassland range—nearly a pure stand of the gramas—and a good range resource. Cattle ranches operate on it as a year-round range. Because it consists almost entirely of the grama grasses, this range may produce a scant growth in years of deficient moisture. Good ranch managers have learned to reserve some of the range, in rotation, for such a contingency.

Most of the range resource that we have considered so far has been privately owned land. Large areas of arid "low desert" land in western New Mexico and southern Arizona are public domain and are not used as a part of ranches. These are seasonal ranges, used by migration from the ranches. As a rule, these lower and more arid lands can be used only as winter and spring range, and they are not dependable for that. In some winter seasons the alfilaria, the woolly Indian wheat, and other usable annuals grow abundantly. In these years, stocker cattle have at times been imported from Mexico in great numbers to use this forage.

As we turn now to the Rocky Mountain region, we see a high interdependence among the different distinctly seasonal ranges and the irrigated feed-crop lands in the mountain valleys. Foothill lands, mostly in ranch ownership, provide the spring and fall range. Mountain lands, mostly in national forests, provide a large part of the summer range. Irrigated alfalfa and native hay meadows furnish the feed for the three to six months of winter feeding and meadow pasturage. Cattle ranches often use only the foothill grasslands for their range. If they use mountain range, it is usually the lower mountain country. Sheep ranches use the high mountain lands for summer range, trailing into such range in late June or early July and out in September. These ranches use sires of the mutton breeds with fine-wool or cross-bred ewes, and market range-fattened lambs. The ranches of this region have high costs, high production, and high incomes. They must be well managed to succeed.

Range lands of the Intermountain region—the region extending west of the Rockies to the Cascades and the Sierras—are of several major range types, and the ranch uses vary with these types. Most extensive of all is the sagebrush-grass range. This type occupies the semiarid country, the lands of intermediate elevation, between the low arid lands, or deserts, and the high mountain lands. It covers large areas of northwestern Colorado, western Wyoming, northern Utah, southern Idaho, eastern Oregon, northeastern California, and central Washington. When in good condition, this land provides all-season cattle range and fall, winter, and spring sheep range. When depleted—as much of it now is, the native perennial grasses having been replaced by cheat grass, an annual brome that is a poor range forage plant—it affords spring and early summer cattle range and spring and fall sheep range.

The next most extensive range land of the Intermountain region is the desert shrub type. It bears usable shrubs, perennial

26

desert grasses, and annual grasses and weeds. We see this range type in southwestern Wyoming, in western Colorado, in the "East Desert" and "West Desert" of Utah, and in central and southern Nevada. Before depletion of the grasses through over-use by range cattle operations, this range supported year-round cattle grazing on a rather large scale. Now the use of this range is primarily winter range for sheep, from November to April.

The mountain and foothill lands of the Intermountain region are of several range types, changing with elevation, moisture, temperature, and duration of winter snow cover. Juniper trees, with an understory of grasses, occupy the foothills, the lower mountains, and the lower plateaus of the Colorado River basin. This lower area is used mostly as cattle range. Above it lie the range types used only as summer range, with sheep using the highest elevations, of the alpine type. Overgrazing by cattle has depleted the grasses in the juniper zone and in the oak brush zone, just above the juniper–piñon pine zone. Oak browse now constitutes a principal, though not a desirable, cattle-range for-age in the oak brush zone.

Range sheep operations throughout most of the Intermoun-tain region migrate between seasonal ranges. Typically, this mi-gration is from mountain summer range, after marketing the lambs, across the sagebrush lands for fall grazing en route to the winter range, and then back across the sagebrush lands in the spring en route to the summer range. This annual trek may cover several hundred miles. Range cattle operations seldom make a long annual round-trip migration between seasonal ranges. Cattle ranches usually operate with a ranch location and some irrigated hay land along a perennial stream or on one of the ephemeral streams that come out of the mountains.

California range lands and ranches are different. The pre-dominant range type is the so-called California annual-grass type. On the lower foothills of the Sierra and on the coastal ranges bordering the Central Valley of California, the annual brome grasses, oat grasses, alfilaria, and other range annuals grow in a green carpet during the winter rains. With the start of the hot and rainless summer, the grasses cure to a dry and a poor feed.

In its lower parts this range is a pure and open grassland. Above this, live oak trees dot the landscape, and yet higher, the annual range plants grow in the brush zone of the Sierras and the coastal ranges. Once this range type had a good complement of native perennial grasses that furnished green range forage longer into the rainless period than do the annuals, especially in the upper parts of this present range type, and provided better cured feed on the range than do the annuals.

Cattle ranches of these California annual grasslands have learned to provide their herds through the summer with protein range supplements, and some ranches own or lease irrigated pasturage in the Valley for part of the herd during the summer. In the autumn these ranches import large numbers of stocker cattle from Nevada, Arizona, and Texas to make use of the large volume of green range feed during the winter. The cattle are then marketed to feeders and packers in the spring and early summer.

Sheep ranches of the California Central Valley breed to lamb in the autumn, market the lambs in April and May instead of in the autumn as do most other Western ranches, and move the dry ewes to irrigated valley pasturage or to mountain range for the summer months. These operations make considerable use of the mutton breeds, for market lamb production.

We turn now to the Pacific Northwest. Range-land resources west of the Cascades are quite limited, as is also the summer range in the Cascades. Central Oregon and Washington range lands and ranches are encompassed in the Intermountain region; the range lands and the ranches of eastern Oregon and Washington are included in the Rocky Mountain region.

Thus we see, in this brief survey of Western range resources, the many and varied natural environments under which the Western stock ranches operate and the consequent adaptation

28

of the stock ranches according to regional location and main range types. We also see the economic changes in the ranches caused by deterioration of the resource. How much farther this trend may go before it is checked and altered, no one knows.

WESTERN MINERAL FERTILITY RESERVES

PHOSPHORUS, a part of every living cell, is essential to both plant and animal nutrition. This mineral is widely distributed through the human body. It is an indispensable mineral from the point of view of the physiologist, the animal husbandman, and the agronomist. Adequate quantities of phosphate in the soil are necessary for the growth of ground cover to prevent soil erosion and to restore eroded and depleted soils.

Nutritional science has but recently become aware of the possibility that phosphate deficiencies in the soils of the agricultural lands of this nation now trend to a point of severity. Excepting some sections of the West Coast and the famed bluegrass regions of Kentucky and Tennessee, most of the soils in the humid parts of the United States have a phosphate deficiency. Many of our soils lacked phosphate in their virgin state; others have a deficiency induced by steady cropping and by soil erosion. We have not been restoring very much of the phosphate taken from the land by farm crops and by erosional losses.

For the year 1944, the estimated total fertilizer use of mineral phosphate in the United States was 1,300,000 tons. Probably we must use nearly three times this amount to check the present trend of phosphorus depletion, and we may find that we must use a considerably larger quantity. A special committee of the Association of Land Grant Colleges and Universities reported in 1943: "Phosphorus is the key element in the conservation of soil fertility," and "the correct uses of an adequate supply of phosphate fertilizer are fundamental to the national welfare, since indications are that at least 80 per cent of the soils of the United States are now deficient in phosphorus." If the per

29

acre rate of application of phosphorus recommended by this committee were made only on the farms of the humid areas of the nation, the annual requirement would be 3,400,000 tons.

We are all concerned in this problem of establishing a permanent agriculture on the essential foundation of a permanent soil fertility. There are economic features of this problem that require national action—the exploitation of farm soils and the slowness in the expansion of phosphate fertilizer output resulting in but slowly lowered costs and prices of commercial fertilizer. Corrective action must come soon. We shall likely need unprecedented amounts of phosphate to change the present disastrous rate of soil losses from erosion in the humid areas. Large amounts of phosphate will be required to restore a grass cover to many of these eroding lands. Without such treatment and a change in use, great acreages of these lands before long will be below the "lespedeza level" for healing and restoration.

The present phosphate bottleneck in the United States can be broken. We have large reserves of this mineral. Even though the present consumption rate were tripled, we have enough to last for a very long time. Our resources of phosphate rock, occurring chiefly in the four Western states of Idaho, Utah, Montana, and Wyoming, and also in Florida, are believed to be almost double the next largest known reserves—in Russia. Limited reserves of phosphate are present in Tennessee, but these amount to only 3 per cent of the total national reserves. Florida and Tennessee phosphate reserves, however, have yielded most of the United States production to date.

Reserves of the Western states are, as yet, almost untouched. Development of these Western resources for production of adequate amounts of phosphate at low cost may have to depend upon a federal government program. With present processing methods, a part of this program would be adequate hydroelectric power from the multipurpose dams of Western reclamation projects. If Western phosphate production can be developed best through government enterprise, low-cost phosphate may then well be supplied on a national scale to privately owned farms as a feature—a very important feature—of public investment in soil fertility and soil conservation.

In the Tennessee Valley area, phosphate has been furnished at low cost to some forty thousand test demonstration farms. These supplies of phosphate are furnished by the T.V.A. through the Agricultural Extension Service. As a consequence of this arrangement, the agricultural production work of the Extension Service has, very naturally, centered around the planning of the program of the individual farm for soil conservation and soil fertility restoration. Perhaps this gives us the pattern that we should use, nationally, in this aspect of our Agricultural Extension work.

Forest Resources of the West

ROUGHLY ONE-THIRD of the total land area of the eleven Western states can be classed as forest land. This acreage is 225,000,000 in a total of 760,000,000. Nationally the percentage is about the same, 757,000,000 out of a total of 1,905,-000,000 acres (excluding Alaska) being classed as forest land.

Acreages of commercial forest land differ considerably from the total forest-land acreages. "Commercial forest land" is defined as land capable of producing timber of commercial quality and quantity and available now or prospectively for commercial use. Western commercial forest acreage amounts to 107,000,000 of the national total of 461,000,000 acres of commercial forest land. This means that about one-seventh of the Western, and one-fourth of the national, total acreage is commercial forest land.

We see from the above figures that the Western states contain 23 per cent of the national total acreage of commercial forest land. But on these Western lands are 65 per cent of the remaining stands of saw timber in the United States. This picture becomes even more extreme when we note that the states of the Pacific Northwest, with only 10 per cent of the national

31

total of commercial forest-land acreage, have 40 per cent of the remaining volume of saw timber in the United States. Of the national total of 44,600,000 acres of virgin-growth saw timber, 41,400,000 acres are in the Western states.

Western public lands account for 63,000,000 of the nation's 461,000,000 acres of commercial timber land. On these 63,000,-000 acres—14 per cent of the total commercial forest-land acreage—are 37 per cent of the nation's saw-timber reserves. Yet these public lands probably have no more than 10 per cent of the nation's capacity to grow commercial timber. Without the sustained-yield management of our Western national forests and other public lands, our timber reserves would likely now remain only in precarious amount.

Our last opportunity to avert critical future shortages of timber lies in conservation and good management of the Western timber lands and stands during the next several decades. It is during this time that we can accrue a growing-stand capital on forest lands of the Southern, Central, Eastern, New England, and Lake states. These states have 75 per cent of the nation's commercial forest-land acreage and a yet greater percentage of the forest-growth capacity. These states now have, however, only 35 per cent of the nation's saw-timber stands.

In the published reports of the survey of national timber resources recently completed by the United States Forest Service, it is shown that of the total estimated 1,600,000 million board feet of saw timber remaining in the United States, 1,296,-000 million board feet are softwoods and 304,000 million board feet are hardwoods. Western stands account for 1,056,000 million board feet of the softwoods, but for only 5,805 million board feet of the hardwoods.

WILDERNESS LANDS

THOSE WHO HAVE EXPERIENCED the wild and savage beauty of Sunlight Basin in the Shoshone National Forest, or have seen an alpine-flower rug along one of the trails of the Gallatin National Forest's Spanish Peaks wilderness area, know the destiny of national forest recreation. Nearly all of the 135,-000,000 acres of the Western national forests have some type of recreational use. Recreational uses of these lands eventually will exceed in importance all other uses, excepting watersheds. Indeed, with this exception, the recreational values may now exceed all other values.

Recreational uses of the national forests are as uncommercialized and unrestricted as is consistent with the development of the recreational facilities and the protection of the resource. It is the policy of the Forest Service to avoid those recreational developments that introduce urbanization into the national forests, and to place as few restrictions as possible on the recreational users. Particular attention is given to the development of recreational facilities for the majority of American citizens, who can enjoy forest recreation only if the cost is reasonable. No charge is made for the use of facilities that do not require special services.

To many millions of people, the wild lands of the national forests afford the only escape from the pressures, restraints, and frustrations of urban living. Recreation in the national forests may be more unhurried and uncrowded and can offer more individual expression than do most forms of outdoor recreation. Yet a large percentage of the recreational uses of the national forests are carried on in areas that can be reached by automobile.

Recreational visits to the Western national forests totaled approximately thirteen million in 1946, and some twenty-six million additional persons traveled through these national forests viewing the outdoor scenes and the wildlife from the highways and motor routes. Areas attracting the greatest number of recreational visitors were—in this order—picnic areas, campgrounds, hotels and resorts, winter sports areas, summer homes, organization camps, and wilderness areas. Besides these recreational visitors, approximately four million hunters and fishermen

33

used the national forest lands, lakes, and streams during 1946.

One or more of the national forests is within a few hours' drive—at most a day's travel—of any point in the United States. Within the boundaries of the national forests are 137,000 miles of forest highways and forest development roads. Located along these highways and roads and along the 150,000 miles of hiking and riding trails, are the campgrounds, picnic areas, and trailside shelters that the recreational users want and need in increasing numbers. Many of the national forest areas that are adapted to high-value special uses—such as ski areas, resort areas, and boating and swimming areas—are reserved and improved for such use exclusively. After improvement of these areas by the Forest Service, special-use permits are granted to commercial developers of ski lifts, lodges, hotels, and other such enterprises, or to associations of users who co-operatively construct and manage such developments. These special recreational uses are now growing at an astonishing rate.

One fairly recent feature in the recreational use of the national forests is the construction by the Forest Service, or by groups of users under special-use permits, of organization camps. Such camps are permanently developed areas with dormitories, mess halls, meeting and recreation halls, water and sanitation facilities, and easy access to a variety of outdoor recreations. Camps built by the Forest Service are operated, as a rule, under the sponsorship of some local civic group. For the use of these camps by organizations such as Boy and Girl Scouts, Four-H clubs, and other groups, a low rental is charged. Duration of use through the season by any one group is limited. There are now four hundred of these organization camps in operation, sixty-five of which are owned by the Forest Service.

One type of recreation greatly prized by some is hiking, camping, and making guest-ranch pack trips in the wilderness areas and wild areas of the national forests. This type of recreation need not be expensive, though pack trips from the guest ranches often are. Many of these wilderness areas and wild areas are easily accessible by foot trail from a motor highway. Wilderness areas are of at least 100,000 acres in size; wild areas vary in size from 5,000 to 100,000 acres. No motorized transportation and no commercial timber use is permitted in these areas. To date, some sixty-eight of these areas, covering a total of 14,978,-000 acres, have been established on national forest lands by the Forest Service. Although this kind of recreational use may never attract large numbers, it seems destined to increase as more people come to know and enjoy it.

Most of the national forest recreational uses are, and for some time will be, however, those that can be reached easily by motor highway. From the highways of California alone, more than four million recreational visitors entered the national forests of that state in 1946. It now is and should be the policy of the Forest Service to accommodate the people who seek, by the increasing millions, the recreational pleasures of the national forest lands and waters. With good planning and development, the recreational uses and values of the national forests can be increased enormously without detriment to other uses and without overtaxing the natural capacities of the resources.

Western Big-Game Herds

Forty years ago the big-game resources on the wild lands of the West were at a low ebb. Inadequate hunting regulations, poachers, predators, and agricultural settlement of the valley lands decimated the herds. But the resurgence of these herds, even though their natural environment is greatly changed, now presents a challenge and an opportunity to wildlife management and to wild-land management.

Something like two million deer and two hundred thousand elk now range on the wild lands of the eleven Western states. Antelope bands, mostly in the plains, may now total one hundred thousand head. Western Texas range lands now have a rather large deer population. Hunting regulations and predator control

35

have saved the Western game resources. Many of the big-game herds have increased phenomenally during the past twenty years, and are still increasing. It remains to be seen whether the science of wildlife management and federal-state law and administration can evolve with sufficient rapidity to avoid a series of debacles such as that of the Kaibab deer herd.

On the Kaibab Plateau of northern Arizona, a deer herd estimated to have numbered originally between twenty and twenty-five thousand increased to one hundred thousand in a span of about two decades. Removal of the cougar and other predators, limiting hunting pressure, and a favorable environment apparently caused this great increase. As this deer herd expanded beyond the capacity of the range, especially the winter range below the rim of the plateau, starvation and disease took their inevitable toll. Now this herd stands at about ten thousand head. Recovery of the range forage of the Kaibab may, in time, make possible the maintenance of a larger herd in healthy condition, but for the present the management objective is to maintain this herd at near its present size.

We see a possible repetition of the Kaibab experience in a number of the other Western game herds because the management policies are faltering and uncertain. Ownership of the big game and the making of the hunting laws and regulations are matters of state jurisdiction. The federal government owns most of the land used by these herds, and the federal agency managing the land has legal authority to protect it from overuse by wildlife. Federal agencies have, however, no authority to permit hunting, since this is a matter of state law. Any killing of game authorized by a federal bureau for land-management purposes must be done by the agents of the bureau. It is clear, then, that an effective policy must rest upon federal-state-local management, but must work mainly through state laws.

Confused and wavering public policies for big-game management result not only from divided jurisdiction but also from the "barbershop biology" of sportsmen who want large game herds and from the uninformed public sentiment against the doe kill to save a herd from decimation through starvation. On the other hand, the users of the lands for livestock range may view the game and the hunters as a nuisance, and yet want the coyotes, bears, and cougars exterminated.

To complete this picture of confusion, we should mention the short-tenure and ultrapolitical characteristics of some state game departments.

Because of this management situation, many of the big-game herds of the West are now in a problem class. Most of the large Western big-game herds have grown past the limiting factor in their environment. Usually that limiting factor is winter range. Much of the former winter range of these animals is now fenced ranch land or irrigated valley agricultural land. Some of the former natural migration routes of the big game, from the summer range in the national forests to the winter range in the public domain lands, are now closed by agricultural development. As a consequence, summer range capacity for big game generally exceeds that of the winter range. Both deer and elk herds now range longer in the uplands than was their natural wont, though they cannot for long cope with deep snow and severe temperatures in the uplands.

Spectacular examples of migratory deer herds grown to management-problem size are the White River herd of western Colorado and the interstate herd of southern Oregon and northern California. Each of these herds probably totals something like thirty thousand deer. The Gunnison herd of western Colorado has reached twenty thousand; the Fish Lake herd of Utah now stands at about forty thousand. Of the elk herds, the Ukiah herd of eastern Oregon, with perhaps twenty thousand head, is probably the largest. Totaling about fifteen thousand each are the North Yellowstone Park herd and the Jackson Hole elk herd.

Perhaps it may be questioned whether the term "resource" should be applied to the Western big-game herds. We know that they are a costly source of meat—they eat some forage that could be used by livestock, they eat and destroy hay, and sometimes they damage orchards and fruit crops. However, this wildlife has high, though largely intangible, values. We might evaluate this resource in terms of the expenditures of hunters, recreational travelers, and others who seek the game; but we know that this expenditure is only a partial measure, and an unfair measure, of the value of this resource. How can one put the dollar sign on the health, energy, and spirit of a people? To quite an extent, these attributes depend upon the vigorous sport of big-game hunting.

Even where the Western big-game herds have increased beyond the capacity of their ranges, their competition with the production of domestic livestock is limited and not of much consequence. The summer range of the uplands is usually ample for the big game, even on those national forests where considerable reductions in livestock grazing are needed for land conservation. Big game, and especially the deer, use the less accessible parts of the mountain country and take mostly the browse and the weeds. On their winter range, where the deer of one herd may die by the thousands in a single season, they do not, as a rule, compete measurably with livestock, which are fed hay and range supplements. Competent wildlife technicians state that where deer overpopulate a range, they compete mostly with other deer; and that where big game do compete with livestock for range forage, it is usually on a range that is used beyond the livestock capacity by the livestock and beyond the big-game capacity by the big game.

Of all the possible moves to attain management of the Western big-game herds, the most important immediate need is to develop an effective pattern for state legislation and administration and co-operation with the federal land-management agencies. National organizations interested in wildlife management could well make a project of evolving and promulgating such a pattern. With this development of good state administration and of technical competence in wildlife management, there would in time come a clarification of major policies affecting the big-game herds. Most important among these would concern the desirable size of the big-game population, the values and use purposes of the herds, and recompense to private landowners for game use and depredations. Finally, state game departments must have effective means to acquaint the public with these policies and the reasons therefor.

II. The West Faces a
Conservation Debacle

Our Exploitative Agricultural Economy

SINCE WE BEGAN as a young nation nearly two centuries ago, never at any time, except during war periods, have our agricultural prices been sufficient to cover the cost of sustaining and renewing the land. We do not need to cite statistics to prove this fact. The reasons for it are too obvious.

Our rapid westward expansion and settlement gave us food in such abundance that the price forced us to work extensively rather than intensively in our farm management. Had our western agricultural expansion been arrested for any considerable time, we soon should have seen a level of food prices high enough to induce intensive farming and much more maintenance of the land.

But since the completion of westward farm settlement, we have seen this situation of cheap food and an exploitative agricultural economy accentuated and extended into the future by new governmental policies and programs. Such programs use public funds for subsidizing the reclamation of arid lands through irrigation and for promoting scientific and educational work to increase the crop and animal yields from the land. Marvels of mechanical and biological science have resulted, but soil erosion and depletion have continued apace.

First and simplest of the answers to this dilemma of economics and conservation springs from a rigorous laissez-faire philosophy. This answer says: Stop underwriting cheap food. Let our "economy of soil mining" proceed with land destruction. Soon the downward curve of land resources will intersect the rising curve of population. Then food prices will have to rise to the point where we will use our remaining lands intensively. And we shall then have the price incentive for conservation.

Would that be the result, or should we then be a hungry nation, unable and unwilling to pay because of high food prices and the cost of long-delayed renewal and maintenance of the land? And as long as minable natural fertility remained in the land, would we not continue the exploiting?

Beyond this laissez-faire approach to conservation economics, we can see two policy alternatives. Both of these are deeply disturbing to those who want an "uncontrolled" farm economy.

One of these alternatives is to stop our "cheap food" programs and hasten the time for management of our better lands at more intensive levels by acquisition of the less productive lands for forestry or for other nonagricultural purposes. We would still produce adequate food, but at somewhat higher prices. As a counterpart of the land-use measures of this approach, some of the cost of private conservation might be underwritten by government programs, with enforcement to insure that the investment in the soil is fully made and not soon thereafter mined. We are, of course, making some effort now in public underwriting of part of conservation cost, through the Department of Agriculture conservation programs.

The other alternative, one which few like but which has some proponents even among those who dislike it, is socialization of all land. Either we do this to the land soon, they say, and save the land, or we do it eventually anyway, after our exploitative economy has run its course and made us a hungry nation.

This point of view argues that our economy will cause us to exploit as long as any considerable reserve of natural fertility remains in the land. Such point of view, of course, denies that effective public controls are attainable except through public ownership of the land. Those who express this belief point to the trend of tenancy and absentee ownership and the constant drain upon the land to provide a cash income for the city-dwelling owner, who too often has little interest in good farm manage-

41

ment. These factors, say the proponents of public land owner-ship, outweigh any higher food prices that are politically accept-able, and will defeat any public programs designed to effect con-servation in our present economic and institutional setting.

FACING THE PROBLEM

THE SCIENTIFIC RESEARCH and the extension work of the Department of Agriculture and the land grant colleges have been very important in making food plentiful and, usually, suffi-ciently low priced to be available to all. But we must realize that this work has not as yet given adequate foresight and study to soil erosion and to the conservation needs of the land. Of still greater concern is the apparent fact that many agricultural sci-ence and extension workers are not willing to face the issue—to see the necessity for reorientation and reorganization of their work for conservation—and even deny the need for soil conser-vation as a major objective.

Our agricultural extension work is organized primarily for the advancement of agricultural production technology. It is assumed that soil conservation will be a consequence of that advancement. Such has not been the result, and it seems clear that we must now place first emphasis upon the planning and management of the farm for soil conservation and adapt pro-duction technology to conservation management. This transposi-tion of production technology and soil conservation in our agri-cultural research and extension work will not diminish the im-portance of production technology, but will adapt it to a new design—a design that we must follow for effective work on soil conservation.

In the past, the operator and manager of the farm has had the help of the extension specialists—the agronomist, the ani-mal husbandman, and the agricultural engineer—in the constant improvement of farm production technology. He has had com-paratively little help in the management planning of the farm, other than for current price and profit objectives. It now seems clear that for the farm operator's interest in the land and for society's interest in the land, the operator's greatest need is for help in management planning to conserve the soil.

This kind of help is now being offered, but as the central feature of an action program which reaches only part of the farmers rather than as the focal point of agricultural extension work, which reaches all farmers. The action program referred to is the farm planning work of the Soil Conservation Service. Skilled observers believe that this approach—aid to the farm operator for conservation-management planning—must be the key to soil conservation. They say that agricultural extension work must adopt this approach—not as just a part of the production features of the agricultural extension program, but as the agricultural extension program. That would, of course, be a far-reaching change, in both organization and point of view, from our present federal and state agricultural extension work. It would be the new design.

In such a design the county extension agent would become the county agricultural conservationist. Rather than being a commodity specialist, as is now so often the case in the production features of the work, he would, in this role of county agricultural conservationist, be a farm-management planner working to relate the alternative production opportunities of the farm to good land use and to maintenance of the soils. His work would be to co-ordinate, for effective farm and land management, the work of the extension production specialists, the federal and state action programs, and the management problems of the individual farm operator in making his farm pay.

Where Time Is Running Out

In the arid western part of the United States, we face a test of wisdom and leadership—a test that is going to prove decisive during the coming ten or twenty years. This test will determine whether we can learn to use the resources of arid lands without destroying them, or whether we shall fall victim to the errors that have overtaken the peoples of arid lands, without exception, in the older countries of the world. We have but to scan the arid regions bordering the Mediterranean to see the results of those errors.

We have a preview of those results now, in some parts of the Western states. We see the great shift in the native plant life of the wild lands and the consequent turn from soil building to soil destruction on many of these lands where nature's balance was precarious. In some extreme situations, we see erosion of a badland character—apparently truly geologic—on sites where it is known by those now living that pioneers once harvested native hay.

These meaningful changes in the plant life and in the soils of the arid West are not localized—they are widespread, the rule rather than the exception. But, like the Nevada ranch youth who could hardly believe that the cheat grass had not always been the most prevalent range plant of Nevada, we shall have to do a lot of learning and a lot of convincing of ourselves. It really is hard to believe that on desert lands of Utah large herds of cattle once flourished—as they did between 1860 and 1890—on year-long ranges.

Large areas of the West can be made barren and uninhabitable in a comparatively short time through misuse of the land, and we are headed that way now. Great systems of arroyos now eat into the soils of arid lands whose vegetation has been given more use than it could take. Upland watersheds that have been overgrazed, overlogged, and burned now yield their waters in an early-season peak flow or send them down in silt-laden floods. Dry-farmed lands of the plains have a temporary respite from the erosion of winds and drought, but the "dust bowls" will swirl again.

Time is short for correction of the present trends in the condition of the land and water resources of the arid West. For most

44

of these lands, there is yet time for correction, but time is running out.

There are instances where it has run out—where corrective action, if started now, would be too late.

Some Say that Soil Erosion Is Nothing New

Some geologists and some soil scientists, viewing the awesome forces of natural erosion that have shaped the features of the earth, seem prone to adopt a "so what?" attitude toward man-induced or man-accelerated erosion of the soils that nurture us. As an extreme illustration of this, one agricultural scientist points to a "good" result of Western plowed-land wind erosion. Prevailing winds carry the soil eastward, fertilizing the farms of the more humid and productive areas of the nation, according to this observer.

One could duplicate many times such observations as this, to show that much of our concern over soil erosion is unwarranted or foolish. There are the rich alluvial flood plains and deltas of rivers formed through water erosion. Some of the rich prairie lands of the Central states are wind-formed. Transported soils may be more prevalent than those formed on the present site.

We can summarize this kind of geologic argument concerning soil erosion thus: Erosion is nothing new. The rock is rotting up in the hills, and this parent material for new soil is being transported to the plains, taking the place of older soil washed and blown away. Furthermore, scientific agriculture now understands the building of fertile soils from raw soils. Why be alarmed over soil erosion, then?

Those scientist-observers who comprehend, in terms of present human society, nature's past formation of soils and man's present use of soils are, however, alarmed. They know that the soils which now support us are the product of a geologic period probably unusually favorable for laying down soils and keeping them in place to mature, comparatively undisturbed.

45

This evidently recent culmination of natural forces has given us soils which we now displace and destroy in "geologic seconds," but which nature produced in "geologic years." What comfort is it to us, who now foresee full use of the soil resources of this world, that nature may in some future geologic era bring forth greater and better expanses of rich lands?

Is it true, as some would have us believe, that a pauperized civilization on eroded and worn-out land is not a result of man's wastage of the soil; rather that the sickness of the land results from an unhealthy human society? This seems equivalent to saying that we know we are destroying our lands, but that we are unwilling to face up to the issues in our political economy which result in the destruction of land.

Let us be open-minded about this. There may be a great deal of interplay between social health and land-resource health. An unhealthy society may breed sick lands, but sick lands will not support a healthy society. Can we comprehend and change the economic and social forces that cause us to destroy the land?

What Is Happening to the Western Range Lands?

"Wyoming's oldest Indian cannot remember a time when Wyoming range conditions were as good as they are this year." This statement was made at a meeting held in 1947 at Laramie, Wyoming, to discuss public affairs and to formulate public policy. The statement was made in refutation of other representations concerning land problems due to overgrazing.

Let us hear what trained and experienced range scientists say about this.

One of the important range types of Wyoming is the sage-brush-grass range plant association. It occupies much of central and western Wyoming. This range type, probably the most important major range type of the West, reaches in great expanses across northern Utah and Nevada, southern Idaho, and eastern

46

Oregon. As a rule, this plant association prevails on the plains, the plateaus, and the benchlands of the Intermountain region, between the low and arid desert lands and the mountainous uplands. Much of this land is privately owned. In some places the ranches hold solid acreages; in other locations the private land is intermingled with public domain. Probably the larger part of the sagebrush type is public domain.

In the natural state of this range type the sagebrush stands were "open." A good complement of perennial bunch grasses and forbs grew in the openings and under the sagebrush. Good range soils were the rule in this range type. The Utah Mormon pioneers soon found that their best dry-crop lands occurred in this range-plant association.

But in this great range resource we see a transformation that is now almost complete throughout the type. We see the bunch grasses nearly gone, clinging to life precariously at the base of the larger sage plants. We see how on millions of acres nature has marshaled the sage plants in closed ranks to cover a soil that would now be bare except where the cheat grass grows. And the cheat grass, a Mediterranean annual that grows early and dries to fire tinder, has replaced the bunch grasses throughout most of this type.

As yet the soils are largely intact in this large sagebrush-grass type of the West. They will not long remain so, especially on the lands that have much slope. Spring growth of the cheat grass in some years produces a sufficient volume of dry fuel to carry a hot fire. In such a year, on a late June day, these fires may dot the expansive landscape of the Snake River plains of Idaho. Competent observers believe that because of these fires the arid sagebrush lands of western Nevada now trend rapidly to desert conditions. Cheat grass-borne fires are destroying the sagebrush and changing the cover to a pure cheat grass. Then when the cheat grass burns, the exposed soil erodes from the hills. Already, in some places, bare basalt shows on the slopes and silt deltas accumulate below the dry gulches and water courses.

47

During the early days of the Western range livestock operations, these sagebrush lands were used as cattle range primarily and sheep range secondarily. Where water was available, cattle thrived on the bunch grasses throughout the grazing season, and often yearlong. But with the depletion of the native grasses, the thickening of the sagebrush, and the coming of the cheat grass, some forty years ago, this use changed greatly. From season-long cattle grazing the use of this range type has now changed largely to spring and fall sheep grazing. The cheat grass makes poor feed when dry, but affords good sheep feed during the brief period of early spring growth. Again in the autumn this range yields some green feed for the ewe bands that come off the upland summer ranges.

Overuse and unseasonal use of this large range resource have wrought the change that we see, and the effects upon the Western range economy have been profound. Cattle production on the ranches of the sagebrush lands has diminished, and the costs have increased. Irrigated pastures and meadows now furnish much of the feed for the reduced herds of these ranches. This effect upon range-cattle numbers and production has been obscured in the statistics by an increase in cattle production on irrigated farms and in some dry-land crop areas.

Methods are now being developed which will make economically feasible the restoration of perennial grasses on the better areas of the sagebrush lands. But on other millions of acres of these lands probably the only hope for conservation of the resource lies in light grazing use or temporary nonuse. This might succeed—granting a series of climatically favorable years when nature would be able to start an uptrend of restoration in this once productive range-plant association.

Most of the other major range types of the West present a picture similar to that of the sagebrush lands. Some of these other types, however, not only have lost most of the perennial grasses but also are losing their soils. The piñon-juniper type and the oak brush type of the foothills and lower mountain

48

slopes of the Intermountain West constitute good illustrations of this.

Probably the only large range type of the West that remains in good condition is that of the Northern Plains—eastern Montana and Wyoming and the western part of the Dakotas. This range type, known as the mixed prairie type, has an association of the mid-grasses and the sod-forming short grasses. This type is ecologically unique. Its response to overgrazing is a diminution of the mid-grasses, an increase in the protective short-grass cover, and a quick economic penalty from the diminished forage yield. Here is one range type that enforces conservation, unequivocally and now.

Wyoming's oldest Indian might voice his guttural approval of the condition, as of 1947, of the Northern Plains grasslands, but they constitute only one of the important types of the Western range resources.

Why Do We Overgraze the Western Range Lands?

One successful rancher, who owns a large acreage of bunch-grass range in the foothills and on the benchlands of the Deer Lodge Valley in western Montana, has kept his ranges in superb condition. They have remained that way through the fifty years he has used them. Yet on neighboring ranges of this same type, the bunch grasses are nearly gone—replaced by cheat grass and weeds. Here is what this range stockman has to say about conservation:

"Though my main operations have been here in this valley, I've also operated range livestock in the plains of Montana— in Wheatland and Musselshell counties, on the Musselshell River. I've seen the ranges of the plains take a lot of beating from grazing, drouth, and even the scourge of the plow, and come back to a pretty fair condition. I guess that in their adaptation to many thousands of years of recurring drouth and heat,

49

grasshopper plagues, and probably heavy use by buffalo, these grasses have become very enduring.

"But the use of these bunch-grass ranges of the foothills and mountains is quite a different proposition. I learned early that in order to keep the bunch grasses growing well on these hills, it is necessary to use them at about one-half the intensity of Great Plains range use. Decline in the bunch grasses takes place gradually, and it seems a waste to use them as lightly as one must if they are to be maintained. Market weights for the live-stock, both sheep and cattle, hold up well even when the range is being used heavily enough to cause the bunch grass to go downhill. You know there must be a limit to that, but it's quite a temptation to use these lands for profit today and not worry about the future. Even the cheat grass that comes in on over-grazed bunch-grass range furnishes quite a lot of feed.

"I'd probably have more money in the bank if I had run more stock on my ranch, but I would now have a run-down range—one that couldn't be restored easily, and maybe not at all. On the plains ranges, the stockmen who overgraze goes broke before the range does, but that isn't true of these mountain valley ranch operations. I've heard my neighbors say that they couldn't afford to graze their range as lightly as I do. But I know that what they call full use of these ranges will not maintain them and that the results are bad, eventually. I've seen those results on comparable lands in my ancestral home, in the Pyrenees."

This man's observations express the dilemma of the use and conservation of much of the range resource from the Rocky Mountains westward. Experimental results tell us that we cannot use more than 40 per cent of the volume of annual growth of the bunch grasses without starting them on a decline and eventual loss of most of their value. But it is unusual, and perhaps too much to expect, for the ranchman to keep his livestock numbers at a level only half what the ranges apparently would carry. Why should he worry about the distant future? Someone who follows him will probably cash in on the land, anyway.

Short-time ranch economics is not a good guide to range-land use in the Western foothills and mountains. It is usually a good guide in much of the plains area. There, because of a different range capacity and livestock management relationship, good land use is good ranch economics, and there is much less lag in the economic effects of overgrazing. A good program of agricultural education and extension work in ranch economics can do much for range-land use in the plains. West of the plains, range-land conservation may have to depend to quite an extent on controls, both private and public, imposed on the use of the land.

Should We Graze Livestock on the National Forests?

In 1914, at the beginning of World War I, livestock grazed on the national forests totaled 1,620,000 cattle and 7,-600,000 sheep. By 1920, these figures were 2,120,000 cattle and 7,324,000 sheep. In 1941, at the start of World War II, 1,207,000 head of cattle and 4,729,000 head of sheep grazed the national forests. For the year 1946 these figures stood at 1,223,000 cattle and 3,703,000 sheep. There was no repetition during the recent war period of the mistake of greatly increasing the grazing use of the national forests as a war emergency measure.

Correction of the results of past overoptimism regarding the sustainable and safe grazing use of the national forests has been a long and difficult matter. Total grazing use of the national forests, including the cut in grazing seasons, now stands at about 45 per cent of the use in 1920. Nor is the task of making the adjustments in grazing use of the national forests concluded. According to a recent statement by the chief of the Forest Service, approximately half of the ten thousand grazing allotments on the national forests are judged to be in unsatisfactory condition and will require some further adjustment in use.

As one reads the printed reports of the recent Congressional hearings on the administration of the grazing use of the national forests, he notes the recurring expression of concern by the officers of the Forest Service over the difference between the present grazing-capacity measurements and the numbers of livestock that once were grazed. Few of the present grazing permittees would want to see the past reductions in grazing use of the national forests restored, yet few are desirous of accepting the further reductions believed by the national forest administration to be necessary for the safe and sustained grazing use of these lands.

There seems no reasonable doubt that the heavy reductions that have been made in the grazing use of the national forests have saved these lands from serious deterioration, both in their range resource and in their soil and watershed values. There has been much less adverse change in range forage and soils on the national-forest lands than on most of the Western range, but the high values of the national forests for uses other than grazing require that there be no grazing use of these lands in excess of that level which assures maintenance of their soils and their watershed values.

A major part of the remaining problems of adjustment in grazing use on the national forests occurs on the cattle ranges. By natural preference, cattle concentrate on and overuse certain locations on the rough upland ranges. For many of the consequent problems of management, no practical combination of fencing, location of salt and water, and riding will achieve a satisfactory solution. In these situations, drastic reductions in the number of cattle grazed have not achieved adequate correction. Certain parts of the range—perhaps a small percentage of the total, yet too important to sacrifice—remain overused. Many of these cattle allotments probably will be closed to grazing use, as the only safe alternative.

Increasing numbers of big game on the Western national forests have been pointed to as the cause of, and the reason for, the reductions which have been made in the grazing of domestic livestock on these lands. Although there are localized situations

Range brush–burning in the California chaparral zone

of competition between big game and livestock on the upland summer range, such competition is not general or very important. Big game use the rough and inaccessible parts of the national forests; their preferences for range forage are quite different from those of the livestock. Winter and spring ranges are the critical ones for the big game.

Range reseeding can meet the problem of range-use adjustments on the national forests only in a limited way. Nature will have to do most of the healing of the results of range overuse on the mountainous lands. The sites on the national forests where reseeding can be done on a practical and economical basis are limited. Rough terrain and the patchy location of overgrazed areas may preclude the use of equipment. Only on the lower and more open of the national-forest lands are there opportunities for doing reseeding to any extent and within feasible cost limits. Total range reseeding on the national forests now amounts to about two hundred thousand acres. Some of this is costly reseeding, with the costs above the economic limits for range use, but justifiable for restoration of an overgrazed range that has high watershed values. Such reseeded range is likely to be closed to grazing for a time, and perhaps permanently. It is estimated that of the approximately seventy-five million acres grazed on the Western national forests, some four million acres could be benefited by reseeding. However, reseeding is not feasible and practical on all of this acreage.

It seems clear that there is no intent, in the administrative policies for the use of the national forests, to close out the grazing use. Rather the policy is, it seems apparent, to make the adjustments in grazing use needed to assure the permanence of the resource and of its uses—grazing included. Some of the grazing reductions have been, and likely will be, drastic, but these actions do not imply a policy of discontinuing grazing as one of the important uses of the national forests. Repeated often in the reports of the Forest Service is the policy of the national forest administration to have the range use make the best possible contribution—consistent with the maintenance of the resources and their highest use values—to the economy of the local communities.

To Burn or Not to Burn

In the great Central Valley district of California, which reaches some four hundred miles from Redding in the north to Bakersfield in the south, autumn fires rage in the brush, or chaparral, zone of the foothills and mountains.

And torrid words rage over the effects of those fires upon the precious few inches of the earth's topsoil—the part of the earth that sustains us.

This natural brush zone occupies a fairly definite elevational scope on the intermediate Sierras east of the Central Valley and on the coastal ranges that form the western border of the valley. To the south of the Central Valley, we see this same natural zone on the uplands west of Santa Barbara, Los Angeles, and San Diego. This vegetative type reaches also beyond the Siskiyous of northern California, occupying about the same elevation on the uplands that form the Rogue River drainage of southwestern Oregon.

In its upper elevations the brush zone merges into a forest zone, though the forest type in the Sierras differs from that in the coastal mountain ranges. Below this brush zone, a belt of grassland extends down to the valley floor. Live oak trees dot the landscape in the upper reaches of these grasslands; in the lower elevations, where the hills meet the valley, the type is an open grassland.

These chaparral lands and the grasslands of the hills below constitute quite an important range-land resource for the California range cattle and sheep industry. It is only fair to say that these brushlands are not high-value lands; that the erosion of their topsoil would not be a loss comparable to the destruction of croplands. Yet any considerable erosion from the brush zone sends sediment into the rivers and reservoirs and often directly into the irrigation systems and onto the croplands of the valley farms.

Forest and range scientists refer to the plant cover of these California chaparral lands as the "Mediterranean type" because of their climatic and ecologic comparability with the similar lands of Spain, Italy, Greece, and North Africa. This Mediterranean type of natural vegetation is one that develops in a climate characterized by hot, arid summers and cool, moist winters. Characteristically a plant community of brush, annual grasses, and some perennial grasses results. The brush plants vary from the succulent types to the hard and woody types. Some of the latter, such as the chamise, are capable of maintaining themselves on harsh sites and sprouting vigorously following a burn.

In this plant association the perennial grasses can compete with the annuals on the better of the soil and moisture sites. But the long and arid summers favor the annuals. Perennial grasses of this type can be maintained under grazing use only if the management is good. Most of the perennial grasses have disappeared from the California chaparral zone and from the grasslands below this zone.

We may deduce what is now happening to the Mediterranean type in California by observing what happened under similar treatment of it in Spain, Italy, Greece, and Morocco. Fire, used periodically to remove the brush and increase the grazing, caused the topsoil to erode from the hills. Eventually the hills became barren and stony—incapable of producing any but the most xerophytic types of vegetation.

Where there is a natural forest zone above the chaparral zone of the mountains—usually the situation for the Mediterranean type of California—fire extends the chaparral upward into the forest zone. Thus, before creation of the national forests in California, the practice of burning the Mediterranean type caused quite an extension of the type upward into lands that are now national forests. Mostly, however, the lands now burned lie below the boundaries of the national forests. These private lands constitute the range land for stock ranches.

In the California Central Valley, the deterioration of the land due to repeated burning is not, as a rule, rapid or spectacular. But where the burning of this vegetative type is on geologically active lands—as on some of the lands of the San Bernardinos and other mountains of Southern California—the results become disastrously apparent. Here, removal of the land cover by fire has caused greatly accelerated runoff, floods, and mud and rock flows, with heavy damage to urban property and to valuable agricultural lands.

Nevertheless, the burning goes on, extensively, in the Central Valley. Perhaps this is inevitable as long as these lands are used for range livestock production. Repeated burning of lands having this Mediterranean type of cover results in a change in soils and plant cover favoring a preponderance of the "fire type" of vegetation. That is, the harder, less palatable, denser-growing types of brush increase, and the perennial grasses give way to the usually less desirable annuals. Burning increases the need for burning, if grazing use is to continue.

In those parts of the national forests where the brush zone had been induced or extended, we see the results, since creation of the national forests, of protection from fire. Grazing capacity has been very much diminished by the cessation of brush-burning. That forest regeneration, though slow, will in time prevail, is the view of the forest scientists. But from some ranchers come demands for use of fire to reopen these lands for grazing. Failure to "light burn" these lands, they say, has caused a stagnation of both the forest growth and the forage production. Is it not significant that the Mesta, or stockgrowers' association of Spain, had sufficient political power during some six hundred years (from A.D. 1200 to 1800) to defeat any opposition to continued burning over of the now barren and stony wild lands of the Iberian Plateau?

Let us note here that the Mediterranean type of brushlands

of California did undergo a great deal of burning in their wild state, before use as range for domestic livestock. Such burning, though, was not at regular and frequent intervals—not every three to six years, as now. Extensive and significant are the changes in the vegetation on these lands; even more important are the changes which we now see in the soils of these lands.

Can the loss of this land resource be avoided without drastic change in the ownership of these lands?

WATERSHEDS AND WATERSHEDS

APPLIED TO THE ARID LANDS west of the hundredth meridian, the term "watershed" has a significance quite different from that of the same term applied to the humid lands of the East. It can truly be said of most of the humid regions of the United States that all lands are watershed lands. In the humid prairies, all parts of a watershed area originate about the same amount of surface and ground water. But in the arid Western states, 20 per cent of the surface area originates 80 per cent of the water yield.

The difference between the kinds of watersheds in arid and in humid climates has a significant economic parallel. In the humid parts of the United States, water yields are, with good land use, usually equal to, or in excess of, the needs of the cities and industries. All of those lands need, consequently, about the same treatment for the related soil and water conservation and flood control. But in the arid Western states, only the mountain lands of great elevation and mass yield any significant amount of water —water that gives life to farms, cities, and industries. These are the lands that must be managed for their watershed function, above all other uses.

This characteristic relationship of the mountain watershed lands of the West to the arid lands—the valleys, benchlands, and plains below the mountain masses—is well illustrated by the accompanying graph, showing the relationship between elevation and water yield for the drainage basin of the Duchesne

The Relationship between Elevation and Water Yield in Western Mountain Watershed Lands, as Illustrated by the Duchesne River of Northeastern Utah

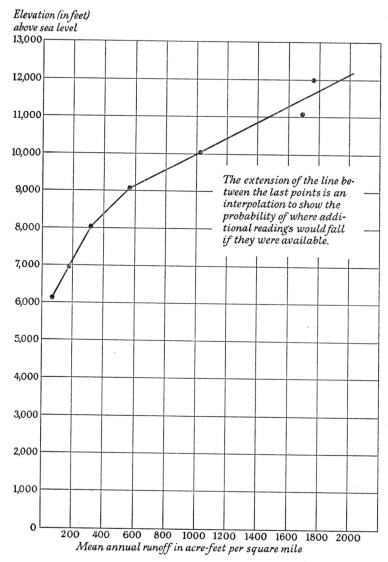

Elevation (in feet) above sea level

The extension of the line between the last points is an interpolation to show the probability of where additional readings would fall if they were available.

Mean annual runoff in acre-feet per square mile

River. This river drains part of the Uinta Mountains of north-eastern Utah. The information shown in the graph came from stream-gage readings on the Duchesne River and its tributaries.

From this graph we can read the meaning of Western water-shed lands. We can see that the lands below six thousand feet in elevation do not yield any significant amount of water. We see that the yield rises to about three acre-feet per acre at the twelve-thousand-foot crest of the Uintas. But the Uinta Basin, whose farms and towns are watered by the Duchesne and other rivers from the Uintas, is very arid.

Hydrologic studies of the Colorado River and the Río Grande give this same picture. Mountain lands above seven thousand feet elevation yield most of the water. These lands, primarily the national-forest lands, constitute only a fifth of the total surface area of the lands in the river basin. This characterization of the Western mountain watershed lands appears to be valid with little or no exception between the one hundred fourth meridian and the Sierra and Cascade Mountain chains.

On the west slope of the Sierras and the Cascades some different climatic influences alter this picture somewhat. Winter rains of the Pacific Coast rainy season reach beyond the coastal ranges and cause the lower lands of the California Central Valley and of the Oregon Willamette Valley to yield significant amounts of runoff during the rainy period. For illustration, the Yuba River tributary of the Sacramento derives not more than half of its total annual discharge from its headwaters in the Sierras above the seven-thousand-foot level. This is, however, a modification rather than a change in the picture of Western mountain watersheds. These valley lands of California and Oregon are nearly rainless through the summer, and it is the snow water from the mountains rather than the winter runoff of the lowlands that can best be captured and stored for irrigation and urban use through the summer.

We see, then, that watershed management has an especial importance for the high mountain lands of the West. Most of these lands are in public ownership—mainly in the national forests, some in national parks, and some in the public domain. Some are privately owned. These watershed lands are of great and unusual public concern. Mistreatment of them can adversely affect the lives of many people, who may live hundreds of miles away and may be quite unaware of their economic interest in these lands. When watershed lands are overlogged, overgrazed, burned, and mismanaged in other ways, the seasonal yield of water may be greatly changed, and the quality of the water much altered.

There are some locations where high mountain lands do not now support, and have never supported, much vegetation. An illustration of this is the "granite country" of the high Sierras. Even in this watershed situation, the pockets of soil and meadow formation perform an important function in the hydrology of the mountain. Without their function, early runoff would be greater, late-season water yield, less.

DESERTS—THEN AND NOW

CERTAIN BODIES OF LAND in the Western states are recognized as deserts and are so named. Some of these are the Mojave Desert of southern California, the Painted Desert of northeastern Arizona, the Maricopa Desert of southern Arizona, the Red Desert of southwestern Wyoming, and the Great Sandy Desert of central Oregon. Just as extensive as those named, though less spectacular, are the large areas of desert land or near desert land in Utah, Nevada, Arizona, and New Mexico.

Although we have no precise scientific definition of desert conditions, they occur when aridity results in close balance or unbalance between the process of soil formation and soil destruction. Desert plants tend to the xerophytic; desert soils tend to be raw and undeveloped.

Much historical evidence gives definite indications that most of the Western desert lands were, in their pristine conditions a century or less ago, in an era of ecologic gain—an uptrend in soil formation and in the succession of plant life. Now we see widespread, rapid, and sometimes violent destruction of these lands in process. We see this in the great washes and arroyo systems that now scar vast acreages of the arid lands of New Mexico, Arizona, and southern Utah. We know that, for the most part, these rapidly forming arroyo systems do not predate the days of the Western open range livestock bonanza following the Civil War. Through the Río Puerco and the Río Salado, these arroyo systems now pour added millions of tons of sediment into Elephant Butte Reservoir. The same may be said of the San Juan and the Little Colorado drainages for Mead Lake.

A recent article points out this contrast in the condition of the now eroded lands of the Southwest: "The original perfection of these valleys was their undoing. In a rare copy of House Executive Document 124, 35th Congress, which is Lt. E. F. Beale's diary of an exploratory trip in 1854 to locate a wagon road through this territory, I searched in vain just eighty years later for reference to the virtually impassable arroyos which now bisect the valley in which he found plentiful grass, and, in the Agua Azul, quantities of fish, although this stream probably does not support a single fish today. He does not mention that his large wagon train was hindered once by the arroyos which now hopelessly cut the route of his march. To him and to countless others to follow, the valleys were thoroughfares perfectly adapted to easy travel."[1]

This eating-out of the age-formed, flat alluvial drainageways of the desert lands is of course spectacular, but of economic importance primarily in the increased rate of reservoir sedimentation that results. Another consequence, not spectacular, is the deterioration of the range plants and the range resource. Many of these desert lands once had a fair stand of perennial grasses; now they have only shrubs and annuals. Within the life span

[1] James W. Deppa, "The Formation and Control of Arroyos in the Southwest," *Journal of Forestry*, Vol. XLVI, No. 3 (March, 1948), 174–75.

of persons now living, some of these lands have changed from a grassland aspect to the grayish color of the desert shrubs. Once these lands could support yearlong cattle grazing; now they require a large supplement of protein concentrate in their use as winter range for sheep.

On some of these severely eroding lands, nature's balance in soil formation and plant development will tolerate only light grazing and good range-land use. It is uncertain whether we can arrest this recently induced arroyo formation in the Southwest.

Many of the desert lands of the West have a high geologic norm of erosion, and the Colorado and the Río Grande probably did, even under pristine conditions, carry a large sediment load. However, there are conservation technicians who venture the estimate that this sediment load has been doubled, perhaps quadrupled. This has, they believe, resulted from the arroyo-cutting in the drainageways and the action of the arroyos as giant flumes transporting the sediment from the head-cutting and side-cutting. These arroyos are dry most of the year, but in flood the samples dipped from a flow may settle out 30 per cent or more of silt by volume.

One nationally known geologist contends that these arroyos have cut and refilled, perhaps repeatedly, in past ages. He states that he has established this fact through study of the soil profiles of the arroyos. His theory concerning what he believes to be the behavior of these arroyos is that alternating periods of arid and humid climate have caused this erosion and refilling. We now are, he states, in a period of climatic desiccation, when it is possible for man's use of this land to start a process that nature would, in time, have started anyway. Thus he believes that man's use of the vegetation of these lands has "pulled a trigger" which nature would eventually have pulled through the increasing aridity. Any discussion of this seems to be useless polemics. Granting the geologist's contention, had not man activated the erosion, nature might not have done so during this geologic period.

The destruction of desert lands through formation of a vast herringbone of new arroyos is one extreme in this picture. There are other desert lands where soils and geologic factors favor soil stability even under widespread changes and decreases in the native vegetation. The Utah "West Desert" lands probably give a fair illustration of this. Once the valley floors and slopes of these closed basins supported a fairly rich plant community of perennial grasses, annuals, and desert shrubs. It has now been demonstrated that through good range management this original plant community can, in most locations, be fairly well restored in ten to twenty years of such management.

There are those, among them some of scientific training, who express a belief that there has been no substantial change in the plant life and no significant acceleration of erosion on the desert lands of the West. To those who have studied the evidence, that belief seems incredible. There are reputable conservation scientists who believe that we are on the threshold of a potentially enormous increase in the sedimentation rates from the arid lands of the West.

There Go Our Reservoirs!

WATER, The lifeblood of the arid West, must be captured and stored expensively and on a large scale in some locations. We see this most dramatically in Mead Lake on the Colorado, Elephant Butte Reservoir on the Río Grande, and Fort Peck Reservoir on the Missouri.

But these magnificent water storages that nurture a growing empire are under an early death sentence. Our use of the land above these reservoirs has greatly accelerated the sedimentation rates. There is as yet no practical method known for sluicing out or otherwise removing the sediment after the turgid waters drop their load into the reservoir.

It was known, of course, when these reservoirs were planned, that the sedimentation rates would be high. We can almost say that the destruction is "proceeding according to plan." How-

63

ever, sedimentation appears to be running somewhat ahead of predictions for Elephant Butte and Mead Lake, and the rate of deposition appears to be accelerating measurably.

Most significant to the future of these storages, however, is the probability that at the time when the plans for them were made and their life was forecast, the sediment transported by the rivers was much more than the geologic normal. In other words, the sedimentation forecasts were based on river sediment loads perhaps double, treble, or quadruple those of seventy-five years ago. So, even though sedimentation may not be running greatly ahead of predictions, there is the possibility that the present sediment load of these rivers can be brought down toward their former geologic norm.

There now appears to be some clear indications, however, that the life of these reservoirs may be even shorter than the early predictions. Concerning the effect of present sedimentation rates upon the life of Elephant Butte Reservoir, a consulting engineer says: "If the average rate of sedimentation shown for the first twenty-six years should continue and all of the sediment should remain in the reservoir, it would appear that the reservoir would be full to the spillway in a total of 158 years, leaving a remaining life of 120 years more. The useful life would, however, be much shorter because the storage capacity becomes inadequate for the purpose for which it was constructed by the time half of its original capacity is lost; at least, its usefulness would then be greatly impaired. This would occur in about eighty years from the initial storage date, or about 1995."[2]

This same engineer's analysis of the sedimentation rates now occurring in Mead Lake leads him to conclude that the "dead storage" of Mead will be gone in twenty years from the initial storage date, that encroachment on the active storage has already begun, and that the usefulness of the storage will be greatly impaired in about seventy years (from 1945).

[2] J. C. Stevens, "The Future of Lake Mead and Elephant Butte Reservoir," *Proceedings,* American Society of Civil Engineers, Vol. LXXI (May, 1945), 610.

What are the possible alternatives for remedial action?

The engineers who have studied the Colorado River point to the several other possible storage sites on the Colorado—higher-cost sites than that of the Hoover Dam—and say that if we are willing to pay the price we can have adequate storage on the Colorado for four or five hundred years. However, there probably is no storage site in the middle Río Grande that offers any practical substitute for Elephant Butte. There are storage sites in the upper reaches of the river, but these sites would be above some of the water sources that supply Elephant Butte Reservoir.

Another alternative is the prolonging of the life of the main river reservoirs by the construction of desilting dams on those tributaries that empty the most silt into the present storage reservoirs. For Mead Lake, these streams are the San Juan and the Little Colorado; for Elephant Butte, the Río Puerco and the Río Salado. Desilting dams appear to be feasible though costly for those two Colorado tributaries. For the Puerco and the Salado, engineering works to spread the flood waters over the watershed, sacrificing the water to avoid the silt, appear to be the only feasible engineering control. Best available estimates indicate that Río Puerco yields about 60 per cent of the sediment and 10 per cent of the water entering Elephant Butte Reservoir.

Finally, there is the possibility of reducing the reservoir sedimentation rates through changed use of the lands where erosion has been accelerated by use. Principally these eroding lands are the lower and more arid lands rather than the foothill and mountain watersheds. Although these arid lands yield a minor part of the water, they yield a major part of the sediment. On large areas of these desert and semidesert lands, the balance between sparse vegetation and soils has been changed. Grazing use has been and is more than the lands can sustain. A lay observer might easily deny this, for great expanses of these lands appear never to have had anything other than their present rate of erosional activity. This activity has reached such a stage on

65

many of these lands that it can not be materially affected in the foreseeable future by any conceivable change in use.

For these lands, land-use measures constitute only a partial answer. Water-spreading and water-holding works and structures on the critical watershed lands and along the drainageways must complement the changes in land use in these situations. One conservation technician made the following comment upon this complementary relationship of engineering and change in land use: "In some critical areas which have been studied, such as the Río Puerco, it appears possible and practical to reduce sediment production 75 per cent or more by a combination of measures to stabilize arroyos, and by grazing control, reseeding where feasible, water spreading, and related measures on the land slopes."[3]

In any measures that we undertake to maintain storage on the large rivers, we must make some choices—choices of economics and of policy. It may be cheaper in some situations to build new reservoirs than to control the sedimentation. But it may not be good national policy to maintain the kinds of local economy that necessitate such choice. Perhaps, on the one hand, we need not have the land use that has caused, and is still causing, the sedimentation. And, on the other hand, we may not need such an expansion of irrigation as may cause us to want all of the water from a watershed even though we must, in consequence, take increased sedimentation.

WANTED: SUITABLE AGRICULTURAL CONSERVATION PROGRAMS FOR THE PLAINS

NATURE HAS SMILED on the Western Great Plains for nearly a decade. Gone are the searing droughts and the roaring dust storms of the thirties. Even the memories of those years have dimmed. Have we at last learned to use this rich land re-

[3] Carl Brown, in *Proceedings* of the Federal Inter-Agency Sedimentation Conference (held in Denver, Colorado, May 6-8, 1947) (January, 1948), 265.

source to avoid its wastage and the consequent human wastage? Or shall we again see that awesome specter of great airborne walls of dust hanging in the sky?

But first let us distinguish some of the regional characteristics of the plains, as a background for a possible regional view of Great Plains land use and land policy. Geologically the Great Plains consist of three distinct regions. Agricultural land use occurs mainly in the Northern Plains region and in the Central Plains region.

From their northward extension into Canada, the Northern Plains extend south to the Platte River, or thereabouts. Physiographers say that the Northern Plains region of the Great Plains ends with the Pine Ridge escarpment in northwestern Nebraska. But for present purposes let us say that the Platte River is the southern boundary, and thus include in the Northern Plains the Nebraska sand-hill country that lies between the Niobrara and Platte rivers. For convenience let us say that the one hundredth meridian marks the eastern limit of the Northern Plains, though geologically this limit is an escarpment east of the Missouri River called Coteau du Missouri. The Northern Rocky Mountains form the western limit of the Northern Plains.

South from the Platte River lies the Central Plains region of the Great Plains. From the Southern Rocky Mountains this region extends eastward about one-third of the distance across Nebraska and Kansas and includes the Oklahoma and the Texas panhandles. Physiographically, the "Break of the Plains," or end of the Ogallala limestone cap, in northern Texas marks the southern limit of the high plains.

In the large view, the Northern Plains should be regarded and planned for as a great range resource primarily and as a cropland resource only secondarily. One may say this even though the spring wheat crop of this region has, in some phenomenal years, been measured in hundreds of millions of bushels. Extensive rough-land areas and immature soils limit the dry-crop agriculture of this large region to certain definite locations. For a guess, 15 per cent of the total acreage of the northern plains has been plowed at some time, and only one-third of this plowed acreage is suited to crop agriculture. The location, area, and extent of that one-third is not even yet well determined.

But it is here in the Northern Plains that scientific range-land management can attain most fruitful results and that a well-conceived program for small-scale irrigation development can make a reality and a success of the family-type stock ranch. We see in the mixed-prairie range type of the Northern Plains a range plant and range soil resource not greatly changed by past use where unplowed. We see good possibilities for range-land re-seeding and for management's success in coping with the climatic aberrations of the plains.

Plans for reclamation development in the Northern Plains should include, to a much greater extent than the present program in the Missouri basin, the kind of small irrigation projects that would serve the hay meadows and pastures of a community of stock ranches. For stock ranches cannot compete with sugar-beet farms for irrigated land to grow hay and pasturage. Consequently the Western irrigation projects of sufficient size for farm settlement do not aid or stabilize a ranch economy for near-by range lands, except that the irrigated farms may sell feed to the stock ranches and buy feeder livestock from the ranches. But these Northern Plains stock ranches can attain much greater stability and productivity through development of irrigation planned as a part of ranch economy. They can benefit only incidentally and in a limited way from near-by irrigation farm economy.

This proposal is not intended to "write off" the cash crop dry-land agriculture of the Northern Plains. Rather, it is argued that the geographic location of successful wheat production can be reasonably well delimited, and that zoning of rural land use or some such control can be used to prevent the cropping of the lands that, though they may occasionally yield well, usually do

The large and important Elephant Butte reclamation
reservoir on the Río Grande, which sedimentation
fills at the rate of ½ per cent of the capacity each year

not grow sufficient crop cover to hold the soil. These "occasional acres" are the roulette wheel of plains agriculture. Some professional agricultural people talk glibly of using such lands in good seasons when wheat is needed and reseeding them to range when not needed. But, alas, nature does not co-operate in restoring a grass cover to a land wind-scoured to the plow sole!

In contrast to the Northern Plains, the Central Plains must be regarded as a cropland resource primarily and a range resource secondarily. These lands that now grow much of the fall-sown wheat of this nation once were a very good range resource. Although there are in the Central Plains rather extensive areas of rough lands unsuited to crop agriculture, it seems a reasonable guess that about half of the total acreage of the high plains has been plowed. Nearly half of our tremendous wheat crop of 1947 came from this region.

Agricultural programs for this region should aim primarily at the success and stability of the wheat farms and the preservation of the lands suited to that use. Here, again, it seems probable that agricultural planning and programing can, and in time will, delimit the areas of successful dry-crop agriculture and preclude or restrict the use of land for cultivation outside those areas. Within the areas adapted to cropping, the programs should concentrate on management to protect the soil. Some of the fertile wheatlands of western Kansas have blown down to the plow sole twice in the past forty years. There is a limit to that. Some not too fertile lands of eastern Colorado that were abandoned for crop farming thirty years ago and that were slowly regaining a range-plant cover are now farmed again, extensively and with large-scale equipment. These lands can be reseeded to a range-plant cover, though neither so easily nor so economically as can the abandoned croplands of the Northern Plains.

In the Central Plains grazing economy, stock farms rather than ranches predominate. These stock farms use the sorghums for feed crops, and fall-sown wheat for pasturage. They have some native pasture land as a rule, but overuse has taken out the mid-grasses and changed the range to a pure short-grass type. This range provides the summer and fall pasturage for the stock farms, fitting in with the grain-sorghum feed and the winter wheat pasturage. However, this range type will, if in good condition, provide a fairly well-balanced season-long grazing. These stock farms operate small breeding herds and buy some feeder animals from stock ranches to use the surplus crop feeds and wheat pasturage. Better management of native pastures could help these ranches to attain a somewhat larger and better breeding-herd operation and, as a consequence, reduce their speculative "warming up" of feeder animals for the corn-belt feed lots.

There prevails in some distinctively range-land areas of the Central Plains a stock-ranch economy, but this is limited. In these areas, the range is not now well balanced for season-long grazing. Management of Central Plains ranges to maintain the mid-grasses as the spring and fall complement of the summer grazing of the short grasses is difficult, but possible. Loss of the mid-grasses turns the range to a short-grass type, unbalancing its seasonal use and making it less productive. Many stock ranches of the Central Plains have, in consequence, changed from a breeding-herd operation to the purchase of yearlings for summer and fall pasturage and sale in October or November. It is to this problem of range management for the ranches and stock farms and to the problem of successfully reseeding of plowed lands that the programs for range-land use should give most attention.

In review and summary, agricultural programs for the plains should recognize two rather distinct natural regions. These regions differ in resources, in the uses that have been made of those resources, and in the corrections that the programs can accomplish. While there is much diversity within these two natural regions of the plains, there is in each of these regions sufficient homogeneity for agricultural conservation programs that fit the lands, the farms, and their future economy.

Coming: A New "Public Domain" in Iowa

MANY OF THE FARM LANDS of Iowa—among the most productive of the nation—are fast losing their blotting capacity, their capacity for rapid absorption and retention of heavy rainfall. The reason for this is the erosion losses from the topsoil and the biotic changes in the soil. Part of the topsoil is gone; the remainder is changed, biologically and structurally.

We can read the story of this change in the lands of the Des Moines River drainage by observing the relationship between precipitation and floods in the river basin during June of 1947. From Fort Dodge to Keokuk, the Des Moines River surged to new highs in flood crests during the latter part of this month. We were told in the news that this greatest of floods was due to the greatest of rains; that this was a flood against which past and future floods would be measured.[4] We were told that the intensity and patterns of the storms in the Des Moines River basin made inevitable these record high crests in the river. This all-time high at Ottumwa was, for example, 20.2 feet, or 11.2 feet above flood stage. Now let us look critically at the facts concerning these floods of the Des Moines. True, the rains were heavy, extremely heavy. From June 1 to June 23 the rainfall totaled ten to twelve inches over a large part of the central area of the basin. Locally a high of fourteen inches fell during this period in a part of the drainage of the Raccoon tributary of the Des Moines. But these precipitation records were equaled and exceeded in the Des Moines River floods of the early nineteen hundreds. One single storm blanketed the lower part of the basin with twelve inches in twenty-four hours in one of those years of heavy June rains and high waters. Unless we can stop the present losses in the blotting capacity of the Iowa farm lands that constitute the Des Moines River watershed, the same precipitation pattern as that of June, 1947, will, ten years hence, send the river to new highs in flood crests.

[4] See, for example, the special supplement, entitled "The Great Floods," of the *Des Moines Sunday Register* for July 20, 1947.

From the highways between Omaha and Des Moines, one could observe, in late June of 1947, the appalling loss of topsoil from the bare cultivated soils of these rolling prairie lands of southwestern Iowa. Sheet erosion, rill erosion, gully erosion—all were evident. These lands that now send the river to new flood crests are in a cycle of more rapid runoff following more rapid topsoil losses. This cycle can be stopped only by extensive changes in the use of these lands and by changes in cropping and tillage for soil management on the lands that are retained in arable use.

Changes in the soils of these lands are, of course, not the only cause of the higher flood crests we are witnessing in the streams of the Mississippi Valley. Ditch and tile drainage of large acreages of farm land now speeds the water on its way. Drainage of swamplands that formerly acted as sponge areas in retarding the movement of heavy precipitation into the river channels has some influence upon flood crests of the streams. These factors, though, are not major influences. They are secondary to the changes in the lands of the watersheds.

Hydrologic studies made in the Tennessee Valley indicate that for storms of moderate duration and intensity, or up to about four inches of rainfall, the peak flow of water runoff may be reduced one-third to one-half by good land use.[5] Good land use is here defined as restoration of a forest cover on eroded hill lands, adequate use of sod and pasture crops, and good tillage and crop cover on cropped lands. These studies indicate that for the storms of extreme duration and intensity, those over nine inches, good land use may reduce peak runoff by one-fifth or one-fourth compared with that resulting from poor land use.

This change in the blotting capacity of Iowa farm lands is much greater in the southern part, approximately the southern one-third, of the state. The reason can be seen by looking at a

[5] Tennessee Valley Authority, "Influence of Improved Land Use on Flood Control and Water Conservation, Upper French Broad Watershed" (mimeographed).

generalized soil map of Iowa. This part of Iowa consists of dis-
sected loess prairies—lands with an undulating and sometimes
a moderately rough topography.

Much of this land should be used for pasture and forestry
rather than as arable land. This part of Iowa seems destined to
become known—and before very long—as "the eroded section
of Iowa." We now see the erosion gashes eating at the hills, the
gray and yellow subsoils showing on the knolls of the tilled fields.

The farm and the community economics of this situation—
the farm finance, the public finance, and the fabric of rural farm
and town living—defy correction solely by educational processes. If this present trend of resource deterioration continues,
as now seems probable, many of these lands will erelong become
totally submarginal for their present uses and for maintaining
the present rural and town economy. What then?

We shall then witness a decadence of rural communities on
the sick lands, abandonment of lands, tax delinquency, and re-
version of lands to the county governments. Here, should this
bad dream become a reality, would be a "public domain" that
would be far more of a public-land problem than are the western
remnants of the federal public domain.

III. Some National Aspects of Western Land Policy

WHAT IS OUR NATIONAL LAND POLICY?

LET US FOLLOW the thread—somewhat frayed in spots—of the evolution of our present policy concerning the ownership, use, and conservation of land.

Soon after the federation of the original thirteen states, all of these states ceded to the federal government, by state legislative enactment, their claims to all domain outside their boundaries. In all, some 268,000,000 acres of land, all of it east of the Mississippi River, were thus acquired between the years 1781 and 1802 as the first federal domain. Subsequent federal government purchases, annexations, and other acquisitions have brought the total of lands at some time a part of the public domain to approximately 1,400,000,000 acres, exclusive of Alaska.

In 1780 the Congress of the Confederation enacted a law that marked the beginning of our national land policy. This was a general enabling act providing for the disposal, by sale and grants, of the territories ceded by the states and for the management and control of these lands by the Congress. Subsequent acts provided for disposal of the public lands by sale only, at first in large acreages. The earliest of these subsequent acts specified a minimum sale acreage of one township. In 1796 this minimum sale acreage was reduced to one section, or 640 acres. These acts specified no maximum acreage, but set a minimum sale price of two dollars an acre. Provision was made for auction sales, with the intent of lifting the sale price above this two-dollar minimum. There was little if any such result from the auctions.

74

Thus we see that the intent of early land laws and policy was to sell the public lands to large speculator buyers for maximum revenue to the federal government. The federal treasury was badly in need of cash. Presumably the settler would obtain his land from the speculator buyers after they had surveyed and divided the land. We should remember that at that time the nation's population was small and was increasing but little. Moreover, the pioneer settler paid scant heed to the land laws. He settled on such vacant land as he chose, relying on his pre-emption rights. These "squatters' rights" were legalized by the Pre-emption Act of 1841 (repealed in 1891) up to 160 acres, provided that the settler paid the government's minimum sale price for the land.

In time there was, however, a growing concern for the settler's desire to buy land from the government in acreage suited to his needs. Consequently, the minimum sale acreage was reduced to 320 acres, to 160 acres, to 80 acres, and finally in 1832 to 40 acres. But there was no maximum limit on sale acreage to any one individual. The government's minimum sale price was reduced to $1.65 an acre and, finally, to $1.25 an acre.

The Homestead Act of 1862 marks a transition in our national land policy—a change from the sale to the spectacular buyer for federal revenue, to the granting of free land to the homesteader who would improve it and make his home on it. This act fixed the size of the homestead at 160 acres. It did not, however, repeal the previous sale laws. During the sixty-year period from 1863 to 1923 the federal land offices sold about 100,-000,000 acres of land under these laws. Sales prior to 1863 totaled some 120,000,000 acres. The table on page 76 gives a summary of the disposal of the United States public domain.

Although the transition to a homestead settlement land policy is clear, there were, nevertheless, some important contemporary modifying influences. One was the enactment of military bounty laws, for the making of grants of land to the veterans of the Civil War and of other wars. Since the scrip for such grants was trans-

A Summary of the Disposal of the Public Domain

1. Sales	220,000,000	acres
2. Homestead patents	256,000,000	"
3. Timber and stone patents	35,000,000	"
4. Grants to the states	242,000,000	"
5. Railroad, wagon road, and canal grants	137,000,000	"
6. Military bounty disposal	68,000,000	"
7. Federal reservations	281,000,000	"
8. Indian reservations	35,000,000	"
9. Remaining public domain	186,000,000	"
Total	1,397,000,000	"

ferable, the acquisition of land under the military bounty laws, through speculative purchase of the bounty certificates, often ran counter to the intent of the Homestead Act.

There were, too, the grants of large acreages as bounties to the railway corporations for the westward expansion and development of the railroads. These grants, totaling 137,000,000 acres, were to be sold by the railroads to help finance their western extension. Presumably the settlers could buy these lands from the railroads at prices no less favorable than those paid to the land speculators during their heyday, before the time of the homestead law.

Yet another modifying influence upon the effectiveness of the Homestead Act of 1862 was the granting of large acreages to the states for their sale for specified revenue purposes. These grants, made under a number of separate acts, totaled 242,000,-000 acres.

The turn of the century saw another period of reorientation in our national land policy.

First, the principle of conservation was becoming a part of our land policy, and as a consequence some large federal reservations were set aside in the Western public domain. This action stemmed from a realization that the use of our natural resources had been lavish, and that large bodies of the wild lands of the West had important watershed and timber values that must be conserved for the benefit of both the Western and the national economy. National forests account for something over one-half of the acreage of the reservations that have been made of these lands.

Next in this reshaping of our land policy were the efforts made to adapt the Homestead Act of 1862 to the conditions of the arid West, but the lack of realism in the approach to the problem resulted in disillusionment.

In these moves to adapt the Homestead Act to the West, encouragement of irrigation as the basis for family farm settlement of the arid lands of the Western federal domain received the first attention. In 1877, Congress passed the Desert Land Act, providing 640 acres for the settler who would develop irrigation. In 1890 this acreage was reduced to 320. Evasion of the intent of this act became too apparent when the "irrigation system" was only a furrow plowed to a dry watercourse. Furthermore, the development of a supply of irrigation water often required large-scale enterprise, beyond the economy of the individual farm. Some eight million acres of land were patented under the Desert Land Act.

Then in 1894, Congress passed the Carey Act for the purpose of fostering irrigation and settlement of the public lands. This act provided for grants to the states of some fourteen million acres of federal public domain on the condition that the states would organize and develop irrigation enterprises for homestead settlement. Three million of the fourteen million acres were taken by the states. About one million of the three million acres have been developed and settled.

In 1902 the Reclamation Act empowered the federal government to undertake the development of irrigation enterprise for homestead settlement. Some two and one-quarter million acres of public land have been developed for settlement under this act, and the federal reclamation projects provide supple-

77

mental water for private irrigation enterprise. The 160-acre homestead size limitation of the original homestead law was carried over into the Reclamation Act.

It was known, of course, that irrigation development constituted only a partial answer to Western homestead settlement—that for large areas of the West the agricultural uses must be stock ranching, livestock farming, or nonirrigated crop production.

As a consequence, the enlarged homestead law of 1909 was enacted, increasing the homestead acreage from 160 to 320 acres in the eleven Western states. This act, though inadequate and almost wholly ineffective, did make somewhat easier the acquiring of the feed-crop and water-source "base property" necessary to the use of the public lands for grazing. Some two and one-half million acres of land were patented under this act.

In 1916 came the Stockraising Homestead Act. This act provided for 640-acre homesteads on lands which the federal land offices examined and passed upon as suitable for stock raising. Besides the eleven Western states, this act applied also to Arkansas, Kansas, Michigan, Nebraska, North Dakota, South Dakota, and Oklahoma. It was intended to apply primarily to Western lands suitable for the production of dryland feed and forage crops. Approximately thirty-one million acres of land were patented under this act.[1]

Thus ended the era of homestead settlement in this nation. The remaining public lands are not suitable for homestead settlement, even in large acreages. They are specialized and seasonally usable lands that require large-scale use and management. Their agricultural uses, especially for grazing, are of necessity tied up with the key feed-crop and water-source lands, which have, in the main, been brought into private ownership under the homestead acts or other land laws. Some of these private lands are in large ownerships and so control the grazing uses, and in some

---

[1] The Kinkaid Act of 1904 provided for 640-acre homesteads, but this act applied only to Nebraska.

degree the other uses, of the public lands. The only means by which a family-farm policy could be applied to these large-scale private uses of the public lands would be to divide the large acreages of the private lands that are necessary to the grazing or other agricultural use of the public lands.

Now we are witnessing what is probably another period of incubation of new concepts in our national land policy. The Taylor Act of 1934 provided for organization of a limited federal administration of grazing and other uses of the public domain lands. But this act made no reservation of these lands from the public domain,[2] and stated that the act should apply to these lands "pending their final disposition." Thus the act is, by its own terms, transitional. We are now witnessing extensive public debate on several issues concerning the direction we shall take in public-land ownership, acquisition, sale, use, and administration.

Several of these currently live issues are significant and fundamental. One of these is whether the federal government should divest itself of much of the present public land holdings through sale in unrestricted acreages to those who now hold tangible use privileges and to those who would harvest the timber reserves rapidly. Another is the reduction in grazing use to conserve the public lands. Yet another is whether the grazing users of the public lands, and especially of the national forests, should have some contractural tenure to give a basis for court review of actions taken by the federal administrative agency. And, as a corollary of this, there is the perennial issue of the relative importance of the different uses of the public lands when the inevitable conflicts between uses occur in our changing economy.

Thus, in summary, we see that our land policy was, and still is, somewhat amorphous—the result of sometimes compromised and sometimes unresolved differences in economic interests and philosophies. But we can and should attain a sense of direction in the evolution of our national land policy by the recognition of

[2] The term "public domain" as used throughout these pages refers to those lands of original federal ownership for which there is no permanent reservation and which are as yet uncommitted as to final disposal.

certain mileposts. Perhaps we now see the formation of one of these, as significant as any of those in the past. That is a growing recognition of the public interest in land use and conservation, and the protection of that interest through public measures relating to both private and public ownership.

Wanted: Unified Policy of Agricultural Resource Conservation

Nationally, we do have, and for some time in the past have had, programs of action devoted to land resource conservation. Each of these has some feature of policy, but we need an over-all policy. We need direction and continuity in the study and planning of conservation objectives and production goals in order to correlate the functioning of the various programs. The programs should stem from an over-all policy, not the policy from the programs.

One means of attaining the needed unification of policy is an Agricultural Conservation Planning Board in the United States Department of Agriculture. The work of this board should encompass not only resource conservation but also the annual and long-range agricultural production goals. The Department of Agriculture's goals programs for national, state, and local crop acreage and production during the war years and since has, no doubt, given some heed to conservation. But the emphasis should be recast. Future planning for the conservation of agricultural resources should be the vehicle for the current production goals planning—should give the needed perspective for such planning.

But as of now our agricultural resource conservation policies are confined to the several agency programs that have conservation as their primary objective. As a consequence these policies are fragmentary.

The Soil Conservation Service of the Department of Agriculture now works with the individual farm operator to analyze his conservation problems and to meet them through a management program for the individual farm. If well conceived, this work can be very effective. But the conservation program lacks national outlook and design. It lacks adequate answers to such questions as, for example, "In what regions can and should agriculture move toward a pasture economy or a forest economy?" It also lacks adequate regional comparisons of the costs and benefits of conservation expenditures.

Our Agricultural Conservation Program—the successor of the A.A.A. crop control program of the thirties—worked effectively through the war period to attain the national crop acreage goals. Payments were used to get needed shifts and increases in crop acreages. But, perhaps inevitably, conservation practices and aims lapsed during the war period. Yet some of the ends of agricultural conservation can be planned for and attained even during war time. Now, if the payments made under this program continue, but for soil-building crops and practices, we have much to gain. And probably this program of the Department of Agriculture could be given a needed individual farm management setting by better correlation with the individual farm plans of the Soil Conservation Service program.

The Federal Bureau of Reclamation, an agency outside the Department of Agriculture, has become an important agency for the conservation of Western land and water. If present plans of that agency are carried out, it will have developed one-half of the total irrigated lands of the West. But we are and have been adrift as far as policy in this field is concerned. National policy programing for agricultural resources conservation could give us some needed answers to questions of irrigation reclamation in the West versus drainage reclamation in the East and South— questions of the present and future needs and values of both alternatives.

One of the recently created federal conservation programs, the program for the conservation and administration of the public domain lands of the West, administered by the United States Department of the Interior under the Taylor Act, has attacked one of the most urgent conservation problems of the West. That problem is greatly accelerated erosion of many of the desert lands and the consequent sedimentation of valuable reservoirs. But the program itself appears ill conceived and very inadequate for meeting this problem. Again we need the guidance of a unified national land resource conservation policy for our program development.

During the hurried agricultural programs of the thirties, the Land Utilization Division of the Federal Resettlement Administration bought some eleven million acres of submarginal farm land. A large part of this was homestead land in the Great Plains—land that had been unsuccessfully used for dry-land cropping. In some parts of the plains this land was intermingled with public domain lands that were, at this time, being placed under the administration of the Department of the Interior through the authorization of the Taylor Act. Here a conflict of conservation policies developed between the program of the Taylor Act and the submarginal lands program. As conceived in the Taylor Act program, the conservation of the repurchased lands would best be served by putting them into stock-ranch grazing, and assigning that use to ranches with a recent operating history in the locality. But the submarginal lands program was designed to adjust some of the grain farms to stock farming by increasing their acreage of pasture and ranch land, and the administrative policy makers of this latter program wanted to fit the public domain lands into that design. Who was right? The right answer was important, locally and nationally. A recognized body of national-level conservation policy would at least have afforded a basis for the answer.

The reservation of the national forests from the Western public domain was a new milestone in our national land policy. These reservations were made primarily for the conservation of the upland watersheds, timberlands, and timber stands. But there are many millions of acres of piñon and juniper woodlands yet in the public domain that should perhaps be in these national

82

forest reservations. And there are other millions of acres of mountainous watershed that may need very badly the kind of protection and management given the national forests. This is another one of the problems for our proposed Agricultural Conservation Planning Board.

The great need is for a live, continuous development of a. body of national policy applicable to our agricultural resource conservation. We should have a good basic design for continuous growth of national agricultural resource conservation policy.

WESTERN LAND PROGRAMS AND POLICIES

RECLAMATION, taxation, and conservation, as they relate to federal, state, and private lands, are the primary facets of Western land policy.

Federal public lands, exclusive of the Indian reservations, account for approximately one-half of the area of the eleven Western states. Public domain lands total more than 180,000,000 acres in these states. About 140,000,000 acres of these lands are now organized as grazing districts under the Taylor Act. These lands and the lease, sale, or homesteading of the public lands not so organized are handled by the Bureau of Land Management of the Department of the Interior. No permanent reservation of these lands from the public domain is provided by the Taylor Act. Homestead entries are still possible, even where grazing districts have been organized, but only after examination and approval by the Department of the Interior. Although these lands are sometimes termed the "unwanted" and the "submarginal" lands of the West, they are in some respects very important in land, water, and wildlife conservation. It seems likely that we shall soon see significant changes in the federal management of these lands—more attention to the public-interest aspect of their conservation and use.

Western national forests total approximately 135,000,000 acres. Most of these lands were withdrawn from the public domain, although some acreage has been added through exchange of timber for deforested land (sometimes for forested land) and through purchase with forest receipts and with funds appropriated by Congress for the acquisition of forest land. The national forest lands were established primarily for the protection of watersheds and timber. About one-third of this land is classed as commercial timberland. Approximately half of the total acreage is used for the grazing of livestock. Recreation and wildlife preservation constitute other important uses of the national forests.

Indian lands, which are not to be regarded as public lands, total about fifty-five million acres in the Western states. Some of these lands have good agricultural resources, and some are low-grade and severely used lands. One example is the Navajo Reservation, where overpopulation and consequent severe erosion now greatly increase the sedimentation of Mead Lake and Elephant Butte Reservoir.

Lands presently held by the Bureau of Reclamation, as withdrawals for possible reclamation purposes, total some ten million acres in the Western states. Western national parks account for approximately nine million acres. Most of this land was withdrawn from the public domain. Wildlife reservations held by the Fish and Wildlife Service account for only a minor acreage of the Western public lands. War and Navy Department holdings for military reservations total nearly seventeen million acres. Submarginal farm lands acquired under Title Three of the Bankhead-Jones Act total some eleven million acres. The Soil Conservation Service is the federal management agency for about seven million acres of this land.

During the past several years there has persisted a live public debate over the retention of these large acreages of land by the federal government. Certain "spokesmen" for Western ranchmen have been the most vigorous proponents of proposals to transfer large acreages of these lands to state and private ownership. Western public opinion appears, in the main, to be opposed to such transfer. Many of these lands have significant public values, and most of them are not well suited to settlement and to use and management in farms and ranches. Probably the total acreage of Western public land is destined to increase rather than decrease. Federal acquisition and rehabilitation of additional acreages of submarginal farm land appears probable. Continued acquisition of cutover and burned-over forest land by both federal and state government agencies seems inevitable and desirable.

Most of the Western state governments now hold large acreages of federal grant lands. Besides the main grant of two sections per township (four instead of two for Arizona, New Mexico, and Utah), there have been some special grants to individual states. Total ownership of land by the eleven Western states amounts to about forty-two million acres, or about 6 per cent of their total area. Original grants equaled 9 per cent of the area of these states.

Rather high minimum sale prices, prescribed by statute, have limited the sale of the state lands, except where they were thought to be suited for crop agriculture. These lands are held for sale or lease by the Western state land departments. Very little attempt is made by the states to manage these lands through the lease contracts, and in some periods large acreages are used without lease. Management by the state administrative agency usually proves costly and difficult except where the land has been blocked through exchange for federal lands or for railroad grant lands or other institutional holdings. Lease prices realized from this land by the states have been, as a rule, considerably less than actual competitive value. Much of the land would sell for grazing use were the minimum sale price restrictions removed.

Federal reclamation development, although now accounting for only two million of the twenty million acres of irrigated land in the Western states, seems destined to become one of the most important features of Western land policy. Several of the large reclamation projects now under way are of tremendous scope, in irrigated land acreage, in power, in potential industrial development, and in possibilities for population growth. Presently authorized projects would increase the total of land irrigated under federal reclamation projects to more than ten million acres, and plans for the future may bring this total to twenty million. It is conceivable that the Bureau of Reclamation, an agency in the Department of the Interior, may become the most important agricultural agency of the West.

Land taxation as a feature of Western land policy concerns primarily state and local property taxes. The property tax policy is of especial importance in the use of Western lands of undetermined adaptation for crop agriculture, grazing, and other uses, and lands saddled with tax policies and taxation not adjusted to their low productivity. There are Western communities which must adjust from a farm economy to a range economy and which are impeded in that adjustment by an unsuited tax policy. There are other areas of low-capacity grazing lands now made submarginal for private ownership by a land tax that amounts to all or more than the "economic rent" of the land and so leaves no return for land capital value. A scientific approach to land taxation can be very valuable to the Western states.

Policies concerning the conservation of privately owned Western lands have, in the main, grown out of the several nationwide agricultural conservation programs of the past two decades. There are, primarily, the Soil Conservation Service programs and the Agricultural Conservation Program (formerly known as the A.A.A.) of the Department of Agriculture. These programs have no doubt stimulated conservation practices and techniques on Western ranches and farms. Examples are the strip cropping of wheat and summer fallow, the reseeding of range land, and the better use of irrigation water. Some qualified observers now state, however, that the A.C.P. programs have accomplished about all they can in their present form, and that they must be recast to emphasize more those needed uses of land and those desirable practices that the farms and ranches cannot and will not undertake without subsidy.

Land policies and their expression through public programs have unusual importance and significance in the Western states. It is, consequently, of especial concern to these states that the policies be well conceived and the programs well adapted and well administered. Some changes appear to be due—and overdue. For example, the programs for the Western public domain and Western reclamation, both of which are now administered by the Department of the Interior, are essentially agricultural programs. They should be administered by the Department of Agriculture, so that they can be co-ordinated, nationally and regionally, with the other federal agricultural programs.

The impact of Western land policy is felt not only upon Western economy but also upon the national economy, and the main outlines of such policy are therefore of national importance and concern. This is inevitably truer of the West than of any other region of the United States.

Future Uses and Values of Western Lands

Because of the immature economy of Western agriculture, the uses, use margins, and values of a large part of the Western land resources are yet to be determined. In the western Great Plains, and in parts of the other major regions of the West, the patterns of farm and ranch settlement—the kind of land use and the type of farms and ranches—are not yet well stabilized. Stock ranching and dry-land farming are, in many parts of the West, the less stable features of the agricultural economy. Western stock ranches and wheat farms have lacked a stable period of sufficient duration, in either their economic or their climatic environment, for the development of maturity and stability.

The states west of the hundredth meridian will, however, evolve forms of economy and uses of land that are unique to

87

the Western regions. One thing that we have learned about forms of Western agriculture and land use is not to attempt to transplant those forms from Iowa, Wisconsin, or Arkansas.

In the not too distant future we can expect to have a much clearer delimitation between the arable and the nonarable dry lands of the West, and to see the evolving of public policies and programs to restore and retain the nonarable uses for lands now mistakenly used for dry farming. We need an early development of policies, laws, and programs for water conservation, and for the allocation of water resources to the most beneficial uses. There must come soon a clear definition of policy concerning public ownership of Western lands and the relative values of the various uses of those lands. It is necessary that we learn how to change the long-time down trend of soils and vegetation on wide areas of the Western range lands. For the gain of both Western and national economy, public belief and public action can and should reverse the present conversion of good timberland to poor farm land and strengthen the management of private forests in the West.

Let us attempt to see how the principal problems of land policy and the land programs briefly outlined relate to the several major geographic regions of the West. Eight such regions may be described: the Northern Plains, the Central Plains, the Southern Plains, the Rocky Mountain region, the Southwest, the Intermountain region, California, and the Pacific Northwest. Each of these regions has fairly distinct characteristics of agricultural resource and land use.

On the Northern Plains, bounded on the east by the hundredth meridian, on the west by the Rocky Mountains, and on the south by the Platte River, we see what is perhaps the most immature and the most variable rural economy of the West. Much of the wheatland now used is intrinsically submarginal though it yields well during the favorable years. Lands on which the soil cannot be maintained and lands which when properly fallowed are not capable of a long-time average wheat yield of twelve bushels per acre should not be farmed. Some type of land use zoning and regulation, perhaps through the soil conservation district, may be the only means short of public acquisition for restoring this land to its suited use—grazing. A high percentage of the Northern Plains stock ranches are not able to cope with the climatic gyrations of this region. Community irrigation facilities for ranches appear to be one of the answers to this problem. Other necessary changes are better range management and a better adaptation of size of ranches to family-type units.

That great winter wheat empire of the West, the Central Plains region of the western Great Plains, billows from the Platte River to the "Break of the Plains" in northern Texas. This region includes southwestern Nebraska, southeastern Wyoming, eastern Colorado, western Kansas, western Oklahoma, and most of the Texas Panhandle. This is the region that became the Dust Bowl during the thirties. It is due soon for a similar transformation. Mechanized wheat operations, often of the "curbstone" or "suitcase" type, again gamble with the climate, wheat prices, and the resources of the land. Such teeth as the soil conservation program once had, have, in some instances, been removed. Agricultural policy and programs for this region need two related objectives—keeping submarginal lands out of arable use and encouraging the kind of farming on the better lands that will maintain them.

The Southern Plains include the Edwards Plateau of west central Texas; the Río Grande Plain, between the Río Grande and the Guadalupe River; and the Llano Estacado, or Staked Plains, of western Texas and eastern New Mexico. The extreme western, or trans-Pecos, part of Texas belongs to the Southwestern region. Excepting the Llano Estacado, the Southern Plains are ranching lands primarily. There is, however, a great deal of crop agriculture, both irrigated and unirrigated. In much of this region irrigation seems likely to exhaust ground-water reserves, and policy and legislation to cope with this problem are very inadequate. Range lands of this region, especially those of the

Edwards Plateau, are in great need of better use and management. Edwards Plateau lands once bore a grassland aspect; now they have a brushland aspect.

From the Canadian border, the Rocky Mountain region extends for nearly a thousand miles south, ending near Santa Fé. The Northern Rockies lie between the Columbia Plateau and the Northern Plains. From northwestern Wyoming, the Central Rockies reach to central Utah, including the Uintas of northeastern Utah as well as the Wasatch Range of northern and central Utah. Eastern and western borders of the Southern Rockies are the Central Plains and the Colorado River plateaus. Throughout the length of this great region, there are valuable land and water resources, concerning the use and conservation of which several important questions of policy prevail. This is a region of great "water export" to other, more arid, regions. Because of the vital importance of these mountain lands as watersheds, their future use will probably be directed toward the conservation of the water resources. Recreational uses will greatly increase, and grazing is likely to be considerably reduced. Agriculture in the mountain valleys will become more self-contained in that it will depend less on upland ranges for livestock pasturage.

Most arid of all Western regions, the Southwest has mountain watershed lands that yield, on an average, less than half as much water per square mile as do those of the Southern Rocky Mountains. This region includes the Texas trans-Pecos country, New Mexico west of the Pecos and south of the Colorado plateaus and the Rockies, and Arizona south of the Mogollon rim. Irrigation has grown beyond the water resource in this region—so far beyond that some of the irrigation economy implies a "tin roof" philosophy for the upland watersheds. This means removal of such upland vegetation as may reduce the water yield of the watersheds, regardless of the severe watershed land erosion and reservoir sedimentation that may result. In this region we see the extreme of ecologic and erosional disturbance of range lands resulting from a long period of misuse. Many of these lands now support only shrubs and annuals where once they had a fair stand of perennial grasses. Corrective measures for the forage and erosion of these range lands seem problematic. The Central Arizona Irrigation Development Plan proposes to relieve the shortage of water in the Gila and Salt rivers by bringing Colorado River water to the Gila drainage, at a cost perhaps greater than the irrigation and power revenues could ever repay. This project has received Bureau of Reclamation approval.

The Intermountain region includes most of the lands between the Rocky Mountains and the Sierras and Cascades to the west. "Arid climate" is written plainly over most of this region. Although this is usually regarded as ranch country, irrigated agriculture constitutes the mainstay of the rural economy. This irrigated agriculture and the urban and industrial developments will soon require the utmost of water conservation and mountain watershed land management. Many of the watershed lands have not had good use, especially the uplands not in the national forests. But the region does have extensive and potentially productive range resources. Although they are, in the general picture, much depleted, most of the main range types can be rehabilitated over a period of time and at a rather high cost. Ranches of this region and of other regions of the West will someday hire the services of consulting range ecologists and range managers.

California's recent, and prospective future, large increases in population have given rise to the most important issues of the state's resource policy—the conservation and use of water resources. The California Central Valley irrigation project will greatly enhance the agricultural and other values of the Central Valley, especially in the San Joaquin area. Probably better information concerning relationships between surface- and groundwater resources and better regulation of the use of ground water will become important features in Central Valley agricultural development. California's range livestock industry is considerable. Most of California's range forage now comes from the

91

annual grasses of the foothills and lower mountains. These annual grasses provide poor forage during the hot and rainless summer. Range management can restore perennial grasses to some of these range lands, to their economic advantage.

Forest land use, although important in some parts of all Western regions, is the chief concern of land policy in the Pacific Northwest. Immense forest resources in this region can be made to yield in perpetuity. Sustained-yield forestry now prevails on many of these lands, yet extensive areas of cutover and burned-over forest lands are burned periodically to keep them converted to range and pasturage. On others of these forest lands the attempts at farming wage an unprofitable battle against the vigorous forest reproduction. The states of the Pacific Northwest could well lead the way in legislation defining the limits of forest lands and regulating their use. Some of these lands are definitely forest land; some may have greater values as farm and range land; then there is a considerable acreage of twilight zone land. A pattern of policy for the classification of forest lands and the regulation of their use such as might be developed in this region could have widespread application in other Western regions.

As the nation approaches the time of economic maturity and full use of resources, it becomes all the more important that we learn the best uses of Western lands. The many prevailing unadapted land uses and forms of agriculture, if continued, can mean only far-reaching losses in Western and national economy.

Taxation Policy for Western Lands

Because of the effect of land taxation upon the economic use margins and, consequently, upon the alternative uses of lands, tax policies have special significance in the use and conservation of Western farm and range lands. Since much Western land is near the "no rent" margin, taxation can make it submarginal for private ownership, even though it is otherwise suited for such ownership. And, in the West as elsewhere, taxes in excess of the earning power of the land are often causative in the overuse of the land. A scientific rural land tax should bear a proportional relationship to the economic rent, or earnings, of the land.

Early Western land policy was transplanted from the agriculture of the prairie states, whence came the tide of homestead migration that overwhelmed the plains from 1900 to 1915. This policy implied that the Western lands could, if necessary, carry a tax load of at least a dollar an acre, without difficulty. This was not impossible for the successfully irrigated farm lands, for their income potential was usually equal to that of the Mississippi Valley farm lands, if the irrigation water costs were not unreasonable.

But we know now that the best of the Western dry-land wheat lands can not carry a tax load in excess of about sixty cents an acre, year in and year out, and that the lowest grade of these lands feasible for wheat production cannot carry a land tax in excess of twenty-five cents an acre. We know now that this twenty-five cent figure for the lowest-yield wheatlands is far in excess of the taxpaying ability of the best of the dry range lands—except the comparatively small acreages of natural meadowland. The best of the range lands, those requiring, on an average, one surface acre for each animal month of use by cattle, do not have a taxpaying ability in excess of fifteen cents an acre. At the margin of quality of range land for private ownership and management—about eight acres of range land per animal month of cattle grazing—the range land cannot carry a tax load in excess of one and one-half cents per acre.

Although the scientific basis for Western land taxes is now developed, the applications are as yet limited. This is due in part to the fact that we yet use land unsuitably; it is due more to unsuited tax policies and to taxation not in line with the earnings of the land. A tax on Western dry lands somewhere in between their taxpaying ability as range lands and their taxpaying ability as dry-farm lands—a not uncommon situation—constitutes an incentive to the breaking of range for speculative wheat farming and a deterrent to the readjustment of submarginal dry farming to a range economy. Perhaps scientific taxation of the Western lands must await the maturing of the best land uses and of effective controls over those uses. However, the unsuited land taxation now prevalent is an important influence in determining land uses, especially in the "shadow zone" between range and crop-farming uses.

Although the now-developed scientific basis for Western land taxation cannot lay down a hard and fast formula specifying the amount of tax per acre according to the various land uses and the quality or grades of land in those uses, it can give an approximation. One way to figure land tax on a scientific basis is to determine the long-time probable economic rent of the land and to fix the upper limit of the tax at one-third of the economic rent. Thus have been determined the per-acre tax standards given above. If the land tax takes the full one-third of the economic rent of the land, the tax then equals an annual charge of 2 per cent on the capital value of the land, assuming that the two-thirds of the rent then available to sustain the capital values of the land be capitalized at 4 per cent. This figure of 2 per cent appears to be a fair guide for the maximum ratio that the land tax should bear to the normal appraisable value of the land.

In the general picture, however, Western land taxation departs from the above approach in two ways. First, the general taxation level for both dry-farm lands and range lands, especially the latter, is considerably above the one-third of economic rent. Second, the taxes tend to an average or a mode for all lands within the use class, rather than varying per acre to conform with the differences in quality—differences in grazing capacity for range land, and differences in bushel yield for wheatland. Thus the Western dry-farm lands and range lands are probably both taxed at a general level one-third to one-half above the maximum justified by their land-rent earnings.

Beyond this, the lack of equalization of the tax according to

94

the quality of the land penalizes the low-yield lands, and so leaves scant incentive for private ownership and management of such lands.

Many Western range lands now paying a land tax of six to ten cents an acre should, according to the procedure set forth above, be paying two to four cents an acre. Ranches on these lands could not long sustain such a tax were not the lands used in combination with federal or state public lands on which the grazing fees and rentals are below actual values. In this situation, public lands pay local taxes indirectly through the private lands. It would be sounder land policy to charge full value for the public land grazing and transfer a share of the proceeds to local tax units in lieu of public land taxation than to subsidize, in effect, some of the ranches by undercharging for grazing and rentals. Inevitably, the prevailing situation causes inequity, sometimes severe, to those ranches that do not share in the grazing use of the public lands. Such ranches are fairly numerous in nearly all areas where public lands are important, yet they are given no reduction in taxation appraisals or assessments to compensate for their lack of public land grazing permits.

Scientific taxation offers a real opportunity and a challenge for bettering the use and conservation of Western lands, especially the dry-farm lands and the range lands. Some of those lands are now overfarmed and overgrazed because their tax level is above the economic limit. The incidence of this is especially heavy on the lower-grade lands because of the tendency of judgment appraisals to stay near a "safe average" rather than to use scientific appraisal techniques based on soils and range-vegetation data, yield experience, and operating income and cost information. Good land taxation can aid in the return of submarginal farm land to range use and remove one of the incentives for changing lands from economic grazing use to submarginal dry-farm use.

IV. Western Public Lands: What and Why They Are

WHERE AND WHAT ARE THE PUBLIC LANDS?

Often the eleven Western states are referred to as the "Western public-land states." In the aggregate, slightly over half of the area of these states is in federal ownership. Besides the federal ownership, state-owned lands add up to a sizable total. These states contain most of the arid lands of the West. As a consequence, their economy, both urban and rural, differs sharply from that of the rest of the nation. Let us view these public lands—the several different kinds of them—as features of the natural environment and of the economic environment of these states.

Of the several different kinds of Western public lands, the greatest in area is the public domain, totaling some 170,000,000 acres. To this may be added another 10,000,000 acres withdrawn for stock driveways, power sites, and other purposes. These 180,000,000 acres are the most arid of the Western lands, but they are not worthless. They support important numbers of livestock and game, and they have some watershed and land conservation problems of great public significance and concern. These lands fall into three patterns of land ownership: (1) the nearly solid public ownership of the low desert lands, (2) the intermingling of extensive private ownership in the semidesert and low mountain lands, and (3) the scattered public lands in the western parts of the Great Plains. Land-management policies for these lands are as yet immature and uncertain. For the conservation of most of these lands and their resources, strong public measures are needed.

Next in acreage are the national forests. Public land in the national forests of the eleven Western states totals some 135,-

000,000 acres. An additional 20,000,000 acres of private, corporate, and state land lie within the boundaries of the national forests. Many of these lands are managed, through agreement with the owners, as part of the national forests.

These national-forest lands are, in the main, mountainous and are often regarded as low-value lands. Many observers express surprise, in their first look at these lands, that such large areas of the national forests are not commercial timberlands. There are large areas that do not grow commercial timber, and others that are too remote and inaccessible for commercial timber harvest. By all odds the greatest value of these lands is in their water yield, and that is recognized in the management policies of the Forest Service, the federal government bureau that handles the administration of these lands. Misuse of these lands, loss of mountain soils, and consequent changes in the characteristics of the water yield could be disastrous to the economy of the West. These lands are, in reality, high-value lands, lands of great public importance. Life and civilization in the arid West depend upon the maintenance of them.

Indian reservation lands total about 45,000,000 acres in the eleven Western states, and 55,000,000 acres in the seventeen Western states. These are not public lands in any legislative concept, but the federal government, acting in a custodial and advisory capacity, exercises a great deal of control over their use and management. Our present policy, as expressed in the Wheeler-Howard Act, is to regard the Indian reservations as a permanent home for the Indians, set aside for the perpetuation of their way of life. Should the Indian reservation, in time, be dissolved, some of the lands could be sold as ranches and farms; others would need to fit into other present land ownerships.

Fourth in total acreage are the Western public lands held by the War and Navy departments. These lands totaled some 17,500,000 acres in 1945. They are used for bombing ranges, maneuver and training areas, weapon-testing areas, airfields, and storage areas. Many of these lands were transferred to the military uses from the public domain, some from the national forests, and some from other public land ownerships. Large acreages were acquired from private ownership because of a location or other conditions especially suited to specific military needs. These lands are now being relinquished from military uses as it becomes certain that they are no longer needed for those uses. Arizona, Nevada, New Mexico, Utah, and California—in that order—are the states with the largest acreage of military lands.

National parks and monuments in the eleven Western states account for some 12,500,000 acres of the national total of 13,-500,000 in such reservations. California leads, with over 4,000,-000 acres; Wyoming has over 2,000,000 acres. Arizona, Washington, and Montana have over 1,000,000 acres each. These lands have high recreational values and have been set aside for public recreational use. As an attraction for travelers from outside the Western states, these lands undoubtedly have large and increasingly important values in the economy of the Western states.

Other Western public lands of some importance are the lands withdrawn from the public domain for possible future reclamation purposes, totaling 10,000,000 acres; the submarginal farm lands, or project lands, totaling 5,500,000 acres; and the lands withdrawn and purchased for wildlife refuges, totaling 3,000,000 acres. Of the lands held for possible reclamation development, the largest acreages are in Arizona, California, Nevada, and Wyoming. Probably less than 500,000 acres of this 10,000,000 acres offer good reclamation possibilities. Approximately 1,000,000 of the 10,000,000 acres are in reservoir sites.

Submarginal farm lands repurchased under the Land Utilization Program total about 11,300,000 acres, nationally. In addition to the 5,500,000 acres of this land in the eleven Western states, there are approximately 2,000,000 acres in North and South Dakota. Within the repurchase project areas, this land was not bought in solid blocks. Much of it has been restored to grazing use and is now leased to the ranches, stock farms, and crop farms that remain in the area. Recently there has been a great deal of demand for resale of these lands, so that they will be available for farming again.

Although they are not large in total acreage, the wildlife refuges are of great importance for recreational uses in the economy of the Western states. Three million acres of the national total of 4,600,000 acres of these lands are in the eleven Western states. These refuges provide resting and feeding grounds for migratory waterfowl, range lands of especial seasonal importance in the survival and management of big-game herds, and sanctuaries for the preservation of rare types of wildlife.

For the most part, the retention of the large acreages of lands in public ownership in the West is for valid purposes, and the public ownership will likely be permanent. This is not yet adequately recognized in the policy for the public domain, nor is there sufficient awareness of the public stake in the conservation, use, and management of much of the land of the public domain. We should have a better definition of policy concerning public ownership and management of the public domain, and of some of the other kinds of Western public lands.

Uses and Values of the Western National Forests

"Forestry," when applied to the Western national forests, must be interpreted more broadly than as commercial timber production. Neither the lower lands nor the alpine lands of many of the Western national forests have any commercial timber production; their forest cover may consist of brush, shrubs, and trees of little commercial value. Yet these lands constitute a part of natural land-use units that do have a high combination of values as watersheds, recreational lands, timber lands, range lands, and wildlife habitats. The enabling legislation for the establishment of the Western national forests from the public domain was especially cognizant of two of the several

99

combined uses of these lands—timber conservation and watershed protection.

Managers of these public lands must continually study and appraise the value of the several uses of the Western national forests. These uses are not, as a rule, exclusive; several uses may occur simultaneously. A range sheep allotment in the alpine country may at the same time be a wildlife range, an overnight camp site for pack-trip parties, and high water-yield lands. Conflicts sometimes develop among these uses, necessitating choice by the land managers.

Natural capacities for one or more of these uses may change or may have been misjudged. As a consequence, such use or uses may conflict with other uses or start some impairment of the resources. Also, the demand for the coincidental uses of these lands may change in a changing economy, altering the relative values and the economic balance of the uses. Here again a choice may be necessary, reducing or stopping one use to make way for initiating or expanding another use of higher value. The objective of the managers of these lands is to keep the several uses in harmony with the natural capacities of the resource and in an economic balance among themselves.

As further illustration of the several coincident uses and values of the western national-forest lands, we note that some 75,000,000 acres of the total of 135,000,000 acres are used for domestic livestock grazing, yet a large part of the grazed land supports commercial timber production. Total acreage of commercial timber land is estimated at 53,000,000 for these Western national forests. Nearly all of the Western national-forest land has watershed values, and nearly all of it has wildlife and recreational uses. Exclusive single-use reservations are minor. Public campgrounds are one such use.

We see, consequently, that forest management as applied to the Western national forests is essentially wild-land management, timber production being one of the auxiliary uses of these lands. In terms of present economy and demand, these lands are

Snowmass Lake from the top of Trail Riders Pass, Holy
Cross National Forest

quite fully used. No attempt is made to "lock up" the resources for some one exclusive use, as is done, justifiably, with the national parks. These Western national-forest lands are made to contribute, within their natural capacities and sustained yields, as fully as possible to the local, regional, and national economy.

As an over-all guide to choice, when conflicts develop among the present uses of the Western national-forest lands, let us look at the economics of these uses. As a first guide, we may attempt to derive an average value figure per acre of Western national-forest lands for each commercial investment in the private enterprise that depends on the use of these lands. From this calculation we derive a figure of approximately $30.00 per acre of national-forest land for the irrigated agriculture that depends upon the national-forest watersheds, $3.50 per acre of national-forest land for the lumber industry that depends upon the use of national-forest timber, and $2.00 per acre of national-forest land for the investment in stock ranches that depend upon the national forests for summer range.

These figures are derived by dividing the estimated total investment of the private business using the national-forest resource by the total acreage of the Western national-forest lands. We must omit recreational use from this calculation, even though we know that it has a high value, both economic and social. Any economic measure of the recreational capitalization value is quite elusive; much of the value is noncommercial and intangible. We also omit the value of urban watersheds in this calculation. Locally these urban watershed values are tremendous, and we are likely in the future to see an increasing acreage of the Western wild lands dedicated exclusively to urban watershed use.

As another measure of the relative economic importance of the several uses of Western national-forest lands, let us compare some estimates of the annual product value of the appraisable uses of these lands. This is given graphically on page 102.

In the preparation of these value figures, the estimated annual water yield of 147,500,000 acre-feet from the Western

Annual Revenue Values of Western National Forests

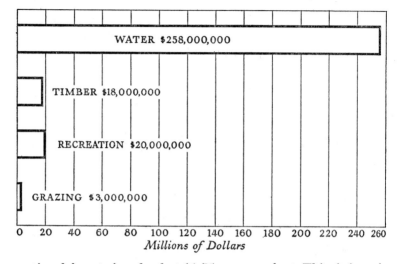

Millions of Dollars

national forests is valued at $1.75 per acre-foot. This, it is estimated, is the competitive commercial value of the water. Some of this water is as yet unused, and some of it is used commercially for more than one use—power, irrigation, and urban supply. The figure for timber is the 1947 stumpage sale receipts. This may be increased somewhat in the future. The recreation value figure is derived by applying private commercial rates to the figures of known recreational traffic or uses in the national forests. Grazing value as shown here is the 1947 grazing-fee receipts.

All of the measures of value of the uses of the Western national forests show the overwhelming importance of the watershed use of these lands. They also assign the lowest value to the grazing use. Here the management choice is clear when conflict between uses occurs. In 1945 the Western national forests supplied a total of 10,466,000 animal-unit months of cattle and sheep grazing of the estimated total of 118,282,000 animal-unit months of beef-cattle and sheep grazing in the eleven Western states. The western economic importance of the national-forest grazing is somewhat more than the 9 per cent which these figures indicate, because of the seasonal use of the national-forest grazing as part of a balanced year-round operation. In terms of the total national beef-cattle and sheep economy, the Western national-forest grazing probably amounts to 1 per cent.

MULTIPLE-USE MANAGEMENT OF WILD LANDS

MOST OF THE PUBLIC LANDS of the West have several simultaneous uses; at least, they can have if managed for such objective. Management should attempt to so balance these several coincidental or multiple uses as to maximize the sustained economic product of the resource.

There are, however, two conflicting points of view concerning the management policy and the administrative organization for the management of wild lands. These two points of view can be expressed briefly as follows: First, the point of view supporting multiple-use management holds that the management officers should be generalists in wild-land management, not specialists in some one of the several uses of the land. Second, the point of view which we might call the functional philosophy of wild-land management maintains that any natural body of wild land should be managed for its one most important use and should be controlled by an agency or organization specialized for the management of that primary use. For the other and subordinate uses, the management agency would then receive management aid, co-operatively, from other agencies specialized in those uses.

According to the multiple-use management view, there seldom need be any one main use or any exclusive use of Western wild lands if the uses are well balanced, and the several uses of the land should be managed by administrative officers who are trained primarily as wild-land managers. Such managers should be generalists rather than specialists in the individual uses— timber, grazing, wildlife, recreation, and watersheds. They must comprehend the interplay of the special fields when they need such technical aid. They should know enough about such technical fields as timber management and wildlife management to know when they need the services of the specialized technician, but they should be management generalists rather than technician specialists.

We see this multiple-use philosophy carried out in the management of the national forests. Forest supervisors and rangers are generalists. They have the services of technician specialists, maintained on the staffs of the regional offices of the Forest Service, and such technicians are often assigned to a national forest where special problems and needs arise. Thus we may say that the administrative organization for management of the national forests is a "line and staff" organization.

As opposed to this multiple-use philosophy, the land-management agencies of the Department of the Interior adhere rather definitely to management by a specialized bureau for the single primary use of land. Then, when secondary uses are recognized for the lands managed by a bureau, the management function for the secondary use is supplied, through co-operative arrangement, by another Interior Department agency or bureau that is specialized in that function. As illustrations of this, the Grazing Service, which was organized to manage the public-domain lands under the Taylor Act, manages these lands essentially as single-use lands, for grazing. It might be added that these lands have important wildlife, watershed, recreational, and other values. The Grazing Service, as the specialist agency, was also given the job of managing the grazing use of the Bureau of Reclamation withdrawn lands and the grazing permitted on the game ranges administered by the Fish and Wildlife Service. Where wildlife management of the public-domain lands appears to be important, such management is, in intent, to be done co-operatively by the Grazing Service and the Fish and Wildlife Service of the Department of the Interior.

It seems reasonable to state that this philosophy of Western wild-land management and the resulting type of administration is something of a tradition with the Department of the Interior.

Perhaps the recent reorganization of the Grazing Service into a Bureau of Land Management for administration of the Taylor Act signals a change in this philosophy. However, the philosophy of single-use predominance and specialist administration has some stout advocates in the Department of the Interior.

Those who believe in this philosophy argue for a "functionalized" administrative organization for the management of wild lands, consistent with the management of these lands for their primary use. Then they say that if such lands do have secondary uses, the administration of those uses should come from another functionalized administrative agency. For example, the Park Service should administer the recreational uses of the public domain. This point of view, carried to an extreme, argues for an administration of uses rather than areas, with the agency that administers the primary use of any one area of land being nominally in administrative control of its own special type of wild land.

This primary-use and functional-administration doctrine of land management has some militant advocates who charge that "multiple use" has become a shibboleth. They say that multiple use attempts to conceal the lack of management and the mismanagement that have resulted from a failure to designate the one most valuable use of different kinds of wild lands and manage them primarily for that use. These advocates would classify and partition the national forests into such divisions as range lands, timberlands, national parks, and game ranges, to be administered by a Grazing Service, a Forest Service, a Park Service, and a Fish and Wildlife Service. Then, should the forestlands need wildlife administration, the Forest Service would get such administration co-operatively from the Fish and Wildlife Service as the functionalized administrative agency for the wildlife. Such is the concept of those who subscribe to the primary single-use classification for wild-land management and a functionalization of administrative agencies to carry out the management.

105

Let us examine this concept critically, and then look at the record. First, let us try to answer these two questions: (1) Will a functionalized bureau, with administrative officers and technicians specialized in one function, recognize the need for, and make a request for, the administrative co-operation of another functionalized bureau for the other, presumably secondary, uses of the wild lands? (2) Is the single-use concept realistic, and may not changes occur in uses and use values so as to alter the position of the primary and secondary uses of these lands?

Concerning the first of these questions, the record says no. The functionalized and specialized administrative bureau does not adequately recognize the management needs of the other uses. It often loses sight of the general-public values such as watersheds; it is likely to concentrate on making its lands single-use lands; it is apt to be reluctant to share its administrative power and responsibility with the other functionalized bureaus which are supposed to administer the secondary uses of these lands.

As to the second of these questions, there are some who argue for classification of the Western wild lands and then dedication of the various areas largely, though not exclusively, to their primary and most productive use. Some who argue for this are to be found among those who believe in the multiple-use management concept and the "generalist and specialist" administrative organization. They say that such land classification and primary-use dedication could add something to multiple-use management and administration. Perhaps some thought and study should be given to this proposal, but the results appear doubtful. Few, if any, of the Western wild lands can be classified realistically into areas of some one primary use, though certain areas may be key areas in some one use. As illustrations of the difficulties in classifying use areas, wildlife uses are migratory, and the domestic-stock grazing use may cover an entire national forest rather than certain areas. Recreational areas and use values may change; even the values of the different timber-type zones and sites can alter greatly in a changing economy. Above all of these uses for most of the Western wild lands, watershed values and problems blanket all conceivable designation of areas and consequent assignment of primary and subordinate values.

GRAZING "RIGHTS" AND THE NATIONAL FORESTS

DURING THE LATTER PART OF 1947, a subcommittee of the House Committee on Public Lands conducted a series of hearings in the western states on the administration of public lands.

At several of these hearings, the chief subject of the inquiry was national-forest administration, with particular attention to the protests by national forest grazing permittees and by their organization representatives against reductions in their grazing permits. These reductions were made by the United States Forest Service, the administrative agency for the protection and management of the national-forest lands. These lands, said the Forest Service officers, could not continue to carry the number of livestock then permitted without loss of plant cover and soils. Unless such reductions were made, they stated, the consequences would be loss of watershed value and other values much greater than the grazing and ultimate impairment of the grazing.

These protests against the actions of the Forest Service followed something of a pattern. There was the challenging of the need for the reductions in grazing use for conservation purposes, backed by the contention that the production and ranch economics of the permittee should be the main guide in determining that need. Then, granting the need for some such reduction, there remained the question of the ability of the administrative agency to determine the needed amount of reduction. This question concerned especially the large reductions. It was proposed that there be a waiting period of several years for further study, and that meanwhile there should be greater efforts in range reseeding and other means for range restoration. Then there were the questions concerning legal and moral rights of the grazing permittee. Typically the grazing permittee owns ranch property—hay and crop lands, water, and seasonal range—the value of which is in some degree dependent upon the use of the national forests for summer grazing in order to attain a balanced year-round operation.

Thus, it was contended, there should be reasonable stability and security of tenure in the national-forest grazing permit. But, it was stated, the grazing permittee has no security in his "rights," and the Forest Service, under the very general enabling act for the administration of the national forests, performs legislative, executive, and judicial functions. It has been proposed, consequently, that there be enacted legislation to give contractural status to, and legal definition of, the private property values in the private commercial uses of the public lands. This, in turn, would afford the avenue for court appeal from the actions of an administrative agency and would, consequently, afford legal interpretation and adjudication of the contract.

In contrast with this proposal, the Forest Service now issues grazing permits which are in no way recognized as "rights." They are issued for a term of ten years—some are issued annually—but no permit is regarded as a leasehold. Rather, these permits are construed as privileges terminable, in whole or in part, if need be for protecting the resource or for changing the use of the land to meet more urgent needs. Also, these permits may be reduced or canceled for violation of the regulations made by the Forest Service. An example of such violation would be placing more livestock on an allotment than the number permitted.

Let us take a second look at this "rights" proposition. There is a fundamental question of government in this, which we shall not try to answer here. That question is whether the development of government-enterprise operation and administration under a general enabling act, in instances where government enterprise involves private enterprise—which we have seen during the past fifty years—is compatible with our system of law and jurisprudence for private property and contract. We have seen that under such an act the Forest Service makes regulations, carries out operations, and makes decisions from which there is, so far as is now known, no appeal beyond the Secretary of Agriculture.

Let us assume that the answer to the above question is yes—since this is the practice being carried out—and that present national-forest administration is compatible with our legal principles of property. Now we are confronted with the sequel question of whether the public interest would be served by modification of the present law and administrative procedure to afford the legislative basis for contracts and court appeal of decisions relating to those contracts. Let us examine this, with reference to the administration of grazing on the national forests.

Suppose that federal legislation were enacted giving the national-forest grazing users a leasehold and a procedure for court review of actions by the Forest Service that affect the leasehold. Would it then be fair, also, to give a water-use leasehold to those whose livelihood depends upon the quantity, quality, and seasonal flow of the water from the national forests? This is obviously impractical. The water users are the entire Western population, or nearly so. Yet these "rights" of the water users can be adversely affected by the "rights" of the grazing users. The public interest must depend, to a large degree, upon the competence and the action of an administrative agency—in this case the Forest Service. The technical formulas for management cannot be written into legislation.

Thus if a grazing leasehold were reduced for watershed protection, on what would a court rule, in case of a court appeal? Upon the validity of the scientific facts, developed and used by the administering agency, concerning the relationships of the grazing use, the soils, the vegetation, and the hydrology of the land? Or upon the technical competence of the administrative agency? It is unthinkable that these leaseholds would not provide for action to protect the watershed values and the other values greater than the grazing values. Presumably the grazing leasehold would give the basis for court determination of damages suffered by the holder if the grazing use were substantially reduced or discontinued. For such damage claim there is perhaps, under some circumstances, a justification.

It does not appear, therefore, that the recognition of a land-lord-tenant relationship in the grazing use of the national forests would result in any gains, either for the public interest or for the grazing user. It is hardly likely that the courts would attempt to rule on the scientific findings concerning the conservation of the national-forest lands, or to devise formulas to resolve the conflicts that will occur between their several uses as the values of these uses evolve and change.

Our present procedure for handling the conservation and uses of the national forests is not perfect; we shall find ways to improve these processes. One Western economic analyst who would substantially change this present procedure decries the "endless bickering in the political arena" that comes from it. But the Congressional hearings and the public debate are a desirable and necessary part of our administration of a government enterprise that must have some flexibility of operation under a law defining the general scope, objectives, and policies of a program. And one faces a philosophical dilemma in trying to apply the laws of private property and contract to the private-enterprise uses in a public-enterprise program, created to function under an administrative agency and primarily in the general public interest.

Lands of the Public Domain

Most of the remaining "vacant, unreserved, and unappropriated" public lands in the United States are in the eleven Western states. These states, as shown by the table below, contain about 170,000,000 acres of public land, of which some 140,000,000 acres have been organized into grazing districts under the Taylor Act. About 39,500,000 acres of the Western public-domain lands outside of the grazing districts are administered under the general land laws and under certain modifying provisions of the Taylor Act. Under that act, these lands may be leased and sold in limited acreages. Homesteading of the public domain, though yet permissible, is limited to lands classified by the Department of the Interior as suitable for the intended disposal under the homestead laws.

Public-Domain Lands of the Eleven Western States[1]

	Within Federal Grazing Districts (Acres)	Outside Federal Grazing Districts (Acres)	Total (Acres)
Arizona	10,164,000	2,501,000	12,665,000
California	3,368,000	13,455,000	16,823,000
Colorado	7,973,000	678,000	8,651,000
Idaho	12,470,000	503,000	12,973,000
Montana	5,920,000	1,821,000	7,741,000
Nevada	33,316,000	12,811,000	46,127,000
New Mexico	15,072,000	525,000	15,597,000
Oregon	12,371,000	3,045,000	15,416,000
Utah	24,970,000	356,000	25,326,000
Washington	----	560,000	560,000
Wyoming	14,454,000	3,208,000	17,662,000
Total	140,078,000	39,463,000	179,541,000

[1] The acreages shown here includes some 10,000,000 acres of public-domain land withdrawn for specific purposes, and so not classed as "vacant, unreserved, and unappropriated" public domain.

These lands of the public domain have important values for both public use and private commercial use. Public-use values, which are destined to increase, are the watershed, recreational, and wildlife values. Grazing of these lands as seasonal range for cattle and sheep leads the commercial uses, but in some locations this use will become increasingly subordinate to private recreational use and to commercial recreational enterprise. Only a small acreage of these lands can ever be used for cultivated crop agriculture.

Concerning the watershed features of these lands, it is estimated that some fifteen million acres yield significant amounts of water and so need the type of watershed management required by the national forests. Large acreages of the public domain are, however, critical sources of sedimentation, even though not yielding significant amounts of water for irrigation, power, and urban use. It is now apparent that large areas of this land must be managed and improved for the primary objective of reducing the reservoir and irrigation sedimentation, even to the exclusion, where necessary, of grazing and other uses of the land.

Public-domain lands afford the winter and spring range for most of the large deer herds that range during the summer on the Western national forests. Additionally, many deer range the year round on public-domain lands that provide sufficient range, as they do in many localities. Western antelope herds, now thought to be increasing, range on the public domain or on a combination of public domain and private land. Public-domain lands also provide the main habitat for several of the Western game birds.

Timberland and timber stands constitute an appreciable part of the public-domain resource. Juniper and piñon-juniper stands are estimated at some twenty-two million acres. Although these stands are not now regarded as commercial forest stands, they afford much local fence and fuel wood. They may become valuable for certain types of commercial wood uses. Substantial though undetermined acreages of the public domain can produce Western yellow pine, aspen, and lodgepole pine and now have some valuable stands of these trees.

Where public-domain lands can be reached from urban centers and are suitable for recreational uses, demand for such uses of these lands will increase considerably. Offering one of the few remaining opportunities for "elbow room," these lands are now in demand for seasonal recreational uses of wild lands.

Probably this is one of those overlooked values of the public domain that will grow surprisingly.

Nearly all of the public-domain land usable for the grazing of domestic livestock is so used. Some ten million head of sheep and one and a half million head of cattle were grazed on the public domain within the grazing districts in 1940. As a result of the war-period shift from sheep to cattle, these totals changed to seven and one-half million sheep and two million cattle by 1945. There was probably little net change in the grazing load. In addition to these grazing districts, some twelve million acres of public domain outside the grazing districts are under grazing lease and are used by ranches as a part of their ranch-land units. Numbers of livestock and periods of use for this part of the public domain are undetermined.

Most of the range use of the public domain within the grazing districts is highly seasonal, this land being used as a wild-land area rather than as an integral part of a ranch-land unit. These public-domain lands are reached by trail migration of the livestock from the ranch base or from other seasonal range areas. The low deserts are winter sheep range; the sagebrush lands, spring and fall range. Summer grazing of sheep on the mountainous parts of the public domain amounts to a large part of the total sheep use. Cattle grazing on the public domain is mostly a spring and early summer use, but it is a yearlong use in some areas. The average period of range use for the grazing-district permits is about five months. Private ranch lands—feed-crop and range lands—and other seasonal public lands provide the forage and feed for the other seven months.

Although the grazing capacity of the public-domain lands is low—present permit use averages about eight acres per animal month for cattle and two acres per animal month for sheep—their poorness is not the only reason, and perhaps not the main reason, why they have not gone to patent under the homestead acts. Many of these lands are not adapted to organization into ranch units because of the necessity for trail migration between

113

seasonal ranges. Where one seasonal range is preferable as the ranch-property base—often true of the sagebrush lands—ownership of that land controls the use of adjacent land, and ownership of the water sources may prove nearly as effective a control. Thus, much of the grazing use on the public domain is controlled through ownership of key tracts and of water sources. Finally, low grazing capacity and value have deterred private ownership and fencing and development for operation of these lands in ranch units, even where physically adapted for such operation. Most of these lands are probably destined to remain in public ownership and management. Measures to further facilitate the selective purchase or homesteading of the better or of the strategically desirable of these lands would result only in a somewhat smaller public-domain residual, a great deal more difficult to manage and conserve.

For and Against the Taylor Act

After several years of incubation, there emerged in 1934 the act of Congress known as the Taylor Act, for the conservation and the administration of the remaining public-domain lands of the West. Now, after some fifteen years of trial, we face a real question of whether this act affords a suitable instrument for the conservation and management of these lands. This question is in some measure due to the nature of the administration which the act has received.

In recommending the enactment of this law, the Secretary of the Interior and his advisers stressed the low cost of administration which they foresaw. They said that the administration could be handled for $150,000 a year, with the help of the available personnel of the department. Thus a basis was early established for the presumption that the management and conservation of all public-domain lands could be approached through ranch management—management of the land primarily by the users as a part of their ranches—rather than through an organization of professional and scientific people trained for the job of large-scale conservation and management of land resource.

This presumption concerning wild-land management was further accented by Section 18 of the Taylor Act. This section, and the interpretation of it in the codified regulations later developed under the act for its administration, provide for elected district advisory boards of grazing users. After election, these board members are given official status by the Secretary of the Interior, and they draw compensation. They are to make recommendations concerning the grazing capacity and season of use of the range and concerning the regulations developed for the use of the range.

In the further development of this idea that the conservation and management of the public-domain lands could best be achieved by fitting these lands into the management of the ranches, the early examinations for the selection of administrators of the act stressed the ranch-operating experience of the applicants. As a rule, the administrative officers thus selected did not have the scientific and technical qualifications for land conservation.

Consequently, in the early stages of the administration of the Taylor Act, attention was focused on the legal interpretations and procedures that would facilitate the concept of land management through ranch management. The terms "grazing rights" and "adjudication of rights" appear often in the hearings for the organization of the grazing districts under the act. The Grazing Code, in defining the qualifications for, and the status of, grazing permits, made these permits adjunctive to the deeded, or privately owned, lands of the ranches. It does not appear far-fetched to say that probably the intention of the early administrators of the act was to fit these public-domain lands into the operating units of the ranches in anticipation of a long-term leasehold or eventual sale of the public domain to the ranches. That intent might be read into one of the phrases of the Taylor Act, which provides for administration of the public-domain

115

lands "pending their final disposal," and does not by its present terminology provide for any permanent federal reservation of these lands.

When a charge for the grazing use of the public lands was agreed upon in 1936, it was fixed at the nominal rate of five cents a head per month for cattle, one cent for sheep. This produced a revenue of some $850,000, but only half of this amount went to the federal treasury. Meanwhile, the appropriations for the administration of the act were increased to about $1,250,000—still less than half the amount needed to do a minimum job of technical land management—and the work of the administrative personnel continued to emphasize fitting the use of the lands into "balanced ranch units." There are, in fact, indications that the ultimate goal of the administrative organization was to become the educational and extension agency for Western ranch management and to achieve public-land management through that means. This possible objective was probably a factor in the organization of some of the grazing districts where the public-domain acreage was minor, or only 15 per cent of the total. In these situations, it seems clear that no districts should have been organized; that the scattered tracts of public domain land should have been leased and sold under the provisions of Sections 14 and 15 of the Taylor Act.

Thus we see why the Taylor Act in time came to be known, rightly or wrongly, as a "Western stockman's law," and why some began to question whether it was doing the job envisioned when the law was enacted. As a result, when increased appropriations for administration of the act were requested, appropriation committees became more and more insistent upon increasing the grazing fees. However, when an attempt was made in 1945 to raise the fees, the move was beaten by the political action of the Western livestock industry organizations. As a consequence, Congress reduced the appropriation to $425,000, or the amount of revenue returned to the federal treasury from the grazing fees. Thus ends a strange chapter in the administration of the public domain. What will be the outcome?

Although the Taylor Act is designed primarily for grazing administration of the public domain, it does contain some recognition of a public interest in the conservation of these lands. Large acreages of these lands have an erosion situation of far more consequence in our national economy than any program for the present management and uses of the grazing. This erosion is shortening the life of reservoirs that serve cities, industries, and farm communities. The erosion-control work will likely require expenditures that make range-fee revenues appear trivial, and may require complete cessation of grazing on some lands.

There are those observers who say that if full advantage were taken of past experience in reorganizing the administration of the Taylor Act, it could provide the vehicle for doing the job. But, say these observers, the primary requirement is a change in the philosophy of land management that has pervaded the past administration. That change would be a change to the policy of managing areas of the public-domain lands as resource entities, not as parts or as adjuncts of the ranches.

Viewing these lands as a part of a ranch unit is not very realistic for either land management or ranch management, for the major acreage of the public domain. Something over half of the 140,000,000 acres now in the grazing districts are desert lands in a more or less wild state. These desert lands are large areas of open range used as seasonal ranges by trail migration; they are not in ranch settlement with the public lands intermingled among ranch holdings. Additional large acreages of these lands—the dryer sagebrush lands and most of the piñon-juniper lands—are essentially wild, though there are private lands intermingled and some ranch settlement. But these private lands are seasonal ranges and are not generally blocked into ranch units. The foregoing objection to management of the public-domain lands through their management by ranches does not apply to the public-domain lands of the Great Plains—to some of the grazing districts of Montana, Wyoming, and New Mexico. But these lands are largely scattered tracts within ranch holdings. They are not large bodies of wild lands used for seasonal range. Such scattered lands should be leased to the ranches, or sold, excepting those tracts that do have exceptional public values.

With this change in philosophy concerning the management and conservation of wild lands, there must be a greater recognition of the public-interest features and values of the wild, or natural, lands of the public domain, and of the necessity for public support in the protection and conservation of these values. Some of these lands will require extensive works for erosion control and watershed protection. Some of them have high wildlife values—they are the winter and spring ranges for many of the Western deer herds. The piñon-juniper lands have forestry values.

Perhaps the administration of the Taylor Act could be changed so that the act would do the job, but the change would have to be extensive. That change would require, besides a new philosophy in the administration of the act, more technically qualified administrative personnel. It would also require a reorganization of the advisory boards and their work, to subordinate grazing use of the land to the needs of conservation in the public interest and to give more recognition to other uses of the lands.

If the Taylor Act and its administration cannot be sufficiently modified and reorganized to meet the management needs of the public-domain lands, what are other alternatives? One alternative might be to supplant the Taylor Act with other legislation designating those districts where the Department of the Interior would continue the leasing and sale of the isolated tracts of the public domain. Then, under provisions of this legislation, the public-domain lands having important forestry and watershed values would be permanently reserved and transferred to the administration of the national forests. In the remaining districts, essentially desert-land districts, these public-domain lands might be permanently reserved and designated as desert-land conservation districts. Since many of these lands will require extensive erosion control, their administration might logically be transferred to the Soil Conservation Service of the Department of Agriculture.

ALTERNATIVES FOR THE DISPOSAL OF THE PUBLIC DOMAIN

PROBABLY the present administrative situation for the public domain is transitory. Neither the provisions of the Taylor Act nor the administrative organization which has evolved under this act appears to fit the management problem of these lands. That problem is, it must be admitted, a difficult one.

As has already been pointed out, these lands are a residual. In the plains, in much of the sagebrush type of the Intermountain region, and in some of the piñon-juniper type of that region, these lands are not in large, solid blocks. The percentage of public land in the grazing districts varies from about 10 per cent to around 90 per cent. Gross acreage of all lands within the boundaries of the grazing districts totaled some 265,000,000 acres in 1945. Only 146,000,000 acres of this is public land administered under the Taylor Act. An amendment to the Taylor Act gives the administration authority to lease privately owned and state lands that are intermingled in the public domain. Some leasing has been undertaken, especially leasing of state lands and railroad-grant lands. No substantial progress has been made, however, in this effort to gain administration of districts where the public lands are in the minority. This land-ownership pattern of the public domain has been a real obstacle to any effective management of range areas and to any administrative accomplishment beyond simple issuance of grazing permits.

Most of the lands of the public domain have had the kind of use common to open and uncontrolled range. As a consequence, restoration and management are difficult. Trends in the condition of the range and soil resources have been down, and this situation is still substantially unchanged. Many of these lands could be reseeded successfully, but at costs probably beyond the limits of the range economy. Even so, some reseeding should be done in the interest of the public values at stake. But the Taylor Act appears to be phrased mainly in terms of a single use for these lands—grazing—and seems not to recognize adequately the other uses or the public values.

Granting, then, that the present administrative situation for these lands is transitional, let us examine what seem to be the alternatives for the ownership and management of the lands of the public domain.

One of the alternatives is to sell these lands, with or without acreage limits, either on the basis of an appraisal or at competitive-bid prices. In such sale the market would, mainly, be the present range users. But it is probable that a great part of the more productive and more favorably located lands that would sell now would revert, in time, because of the high cost, per unit of capacity, of owning low-grade and highly seasonal range land. Sale of the public domain would imply that the public values and interests in the restoration and management of these lands would be safeguarded through ranch ownership and operation. For the lands that would not sell—the residual of the residual—some kind of public administration would still be needed.

Another alternative sometimes proposed for the lands of the public domain is a careful classification study to determine their fitness for sale, lease, and retention in public ownership and management. Some percentage of these lands, it is argued, should be capable of successful private ownership, and should be in such ownership unless public values and significant public interests are involved in the lands. Such a study might recommend, for example, that most of the scattered and isolated tracts of the public domain be sold; that certain types of land be leased for a term of years and under specified restrictions; and that

120

certain other types be held, managed, and developed in the public interest, with grazing and other private uses secondary. The results of such a study could be just as undesirable as they could be desirable. The study should be made only by those who have an ample comprehension of the conservation requirements of the lands and an understanding of the adapted patterns of land management.

Yet another possibility for change from the present situation in the handling of the public domain would be to sell the scattered tracts and then—with adequate provisions for exchange, acquisition, and sale—to block out manageable areas, make permanent public reservation of the principal acreages, and assign the management of the unsold lands to the suited land-management agencies of the Department of Agriculture. Thus the lands with forest and upland-watershed values would be added to the national forests, the lands requiring rehabilitation—management for soil conservation and alleviation of reservoir sedimentation—or other development in the public interest, would be managed by the Soil Conservation Service. Grazing and other private uses would be handled in accordance with the regulations of these agencies.

Still another alternative is to attempt to correct the faults of the present legislation and administration for the management of the public domain. This alternative has already been developed at length.

Western Indian Reservations

Indian reservations embrace approximately fifty-five million acres of land in the seventeen Western states. These lands have been set aside by federal government treaties and by executive orders making withdrawals from the public domain for Indian reservations. Except for a minor acreage, these are not public lands. They are held in tribal ownerships, in "trust patents" for individual Indian owners (by the Indian Service),

121

and in fee ownerships by individual Indian owners. It was originally provided that the trust patents should mature into fee ownerships in twenty-five years. Recent legislation has changed this, however, to limit the maturity of the trust patents and the consequent opportunity for sale of lands by individual fee owners.

The Indian Service, which administers the legislation and the programs for Indian reservations, maintains headquarters for its several functions at each of the reservations. Functions of this federal bureau include working with the tribal organizations for leasing of lands, for irrigation and other land-development projects, for operation of schools, and for law enforcement. This bureau does agricultural extension work with the Indians and administers a program for Indian agricultural finance. There are a number of technical and trade schools away from the Indian reservations and administered apart from the reservations.

Lands of the Indian reservations vary from good to very poor as range and cropland resources. Probably half of the nearly seventeen million acres of the Navajo Reservation may be classed as barren. Several of the northern reservations have good range and farm lands. Examples of this are the Blackfoot Reservation in Idaho, the Crow Reservation in Montana, and the Rosebud Reservation in South Dakota.

In all the reservations, lands now under irrigation total 829,000 acres. Of these, 539,000 acres are Indian owned and 290,000 acres are in non-Indian ownership. Total potential irrigation development on the Indian reservations is estimated at 1,700,000 acres, of which 1,300,000 acres would be in Indian ownership.

There are two opposing points of view concerning the policy that should be followed in the administration of Indian affairs by the federal government. One of these would aim primarily to maintain the Indian communities and the tribal organization, government, and culture on the reservations, and, though it would not seek to prevent, would not encourage, migration of the Indians from the reservation and their assimilation. The other policy would facilitate sale of lands by Indian owners and the eventual dissolution of the reservations and reservation administrations. This would mean the breakup of tribal organizations and tribal culture. Such a policy would likely require additional programs for education and training and for placement in jobs and relocation off the reservations.

Under the Wheeler-Howard legislation, known as the Indian Reorganization Act, our policy appears definitely to be the former of the two described above. It seems desirable, however, that the policy now contained in legislation be reoriented toward migration and assimilation. The Indian population on the Western reservations now stands at about 300,000 and, especially for certain tribes, the population trend is decidedly upward.

WESTERN NATIONAL PARKS AND NATIONAL MONUMENTS

LANDS OF THE WESTERN STATES in national parks and national monuments total some 12,500,000 acres in the national total of 13,600,000 acres. These Western national parks and national monuments have been created, for the most part, from the public domain, the national forests, and other public lands by Presidential executive order. National parks and national monuments are under the administration of the Park Service of the Department of the Interior.

Policy in the creation of the national parks has stressed the selection of large bodies of wild lands having high scenic and recreational values and natural features of unusual interest. Location for easy access by rail and motor transportation has also been regarded as important. Commercial uses of the resources, such as grazing, logging, and mining, are prohibited. The policy concerning private commercial concessions within the parks for meals and lodging, transportation, and merchandising varies considerably. Specifications for such policy are drafted in the executive order creating each park. For example, there are scarcely

123

any private commercial concessions within the boundaries of Rocky Mountain National Park, while those of Yellowstone are many and magnificent. Fine hotels are available in Yellowstone for those who want their wilderness in luxury, but the Park Service also provides public campgrounds for those who wish to rough it.

National monuments, usually of limited area, are selected for the preservation of sites that have unusual natural phenomena, historical interest, or scenic value. They are not large bodies of recreational wilderness lands and presumably are not created primarily for recreational use, though that use may be important. Limited commercial use of the resources may be allowed in the area if such use is compatible with the preservation of those features of the resource for which the monument was created. Location for easy access by motor highway is not regarded as essential in the creation of national monuments. Roads for access by recreational travelers are being constructed, however, where the demand seems sufficient.

Some observers of Western land use feel that the Western national parks have become overcommercialized and overregulated and that, as a consequence, they do not afford a good opportunity for unregimented enjoyment of wild lands. For those parks that receive large amounts of visitors, that type of enjoyment is probably too much to expect. The large numbers of motor tourists who want to see the wilderness from the highways, rather than the much smaller number who enter it by trail to really savor it, must now come first in the thinking and planning of the National Park Service.

THE "L–U" LANDS

DURING THE PERIOD 1935 to 1945 the federal government acquired, under various legislative authorizations, some eleven and one-third million acres of land in a program of land-use adjustment. Most of these lands were selected as being submarginal for their present use as farm land. Objectives of this program were to give "stranded" farm people an opportunity to relocate, to restore the land to its suitable uses, and to fit the restored lands into an adjustment of the remaining farm units and the type of agriculture. This program has been called the Land Utilization Program, the acquired lands the "L–U" lands, and the areas in which lands were acquired the "L–U" project areas.

These project areas were located in forty-five states, but the greatest activity was in the western Great Plains, and over half of the land acquired was in the plains states. In the plains states the primary land-use objective was to restore the land to better-adapted uses than dry farming, and usually this use was grazing. Elsewhere than in the plains—and to some extent in the plains—a part of the lands acquired were suitable primarily for public administration as wildlife, recreational, or forest lands and were transferred to federal public-land administrative agencies for these purposes. Such transfers total approximately three million acres. Another million acres of the L–U lands have been made available to state administrative agencies, under federal-state agreements concerning the use of these lands. More than seven million acres of the total eleven and one-third millions are now managed by the Soil Conservation Service, the federal administrative agency for the program.

In the organization of the L–U project areas, general boundaries were first set. These boundaries included much more land than was to be purchased, for the intent was to acquire mainly the "distress" lands. Selection for purchase sought to avoid disturbance of lands in reasonably good use and of farms that were adapted or capable of adaptation through use of the acquired lands after restoration and development of those lands. Fences and buildings were removed from the acquired lands, reseeding was undertaken to restore a range cover on the plowed lands, and water was developed for the grazing use and management of the acquired lands.

125

In fitting the use of the L–U lands into a plan for strengthening the farms and ranches remaining in the project area, local organizations, such as soil-conservation districts and state grazing districts, participated actively. These local organizations now participate in the management of the L–U lands used as community grazing allotments. Thus the acquired lands are used in close association with the private lands of the project areas. The acquired lands have been important in changing the land use and in adjusting and strengthening the economy of project areas.

The L–U Program has not been large in terms of total Western public-land acreage, but it is significant far beyond its proportionate acreage. We may see a revival of this program in the future, though the land-acquisition phase is now at a standstill and we hear proposals to resell the L–U lands to private users for dry farming. During the past decade of generally favorable years in the plains states, we have forgotten much of the need for this program and of its accomplishments, which are far reaching and real in most of the project areas.

By far the best alternative, both for the project areas and for our total economy, appears to be to keep these "shadow zone" lands in public ownership and under such term uses by the farms and ranches of the areas as will protect these lands from a repetition of the past mistakes in their use. Meanwhile, perhaps we had better keep this L–U Program in a good state of repair. We may want it again.

County and Local Tax Revenues from Rural Public Lands

There is at present no uniform or consistent policy for payment by the federal government to the state, county, or local tax units a specified sum in lieu of taxes on federal public lands, or for permitting these lands to be taxed.

Where such payments are made, the rates appear low in comparison with private land taxes. For example, the rate for

126

the national-forest lands amounts to one or two cents an acre, which goes to the counties for roads and schools, but this seemingly low figure is 25 per cent of the national-forest receipts. Out of the present low grazing fee of eight cents per animal-unit month from the public-domain grazing districts administered under the Taylor Act, three-fourths of a cent goes to the county in lieu of taxes. Almost no state governments have a policy for payments to local government in lieu of taxes on state-owned lands. As a consequence of this situation, there are instances where Western county and local tax units have a small tax base and a low tax revenue that appear to be compensated only partially by the federal payments in lieu of taxes. Various proposals have been made to correct this apparent inequity. One is to increase the federal revenues from the land and to increase the share paid to counties in lieu of taxes to as much as 50 per cent of the total revenue. Another proposal would permit taxation of the public lands by state, county, and local tax units on the same basis as the privately owned lands. Currently the most active proposal and the one receiving the most legislative attention would fix an appraised value for federally-owned real estate and would pay to the local tax units, in lieu of taxes, an annual percentage on that value. This percentage has varied in the proposals from three-fourths of 1 per cent to 3 per cent.

Let us examine this question and the alternative proposals a bit critically and skeptically. Could it be that there are some present indirect compensations from the federal public lands to the county tax revenues? Might there be a desire to shift some of the incidence of local taxation to the federal treasury, using the federal public lands as the medium for such a shift? First let us look at some information concerning the present situation, in which, we must agree, the policy is unsettled and not consistent among the various kinds of federal public-land ownerships.

Studies that have been made of this subject for the national forests indicate that the contributions from those lands in support of state and local finance have been substantial—more, in fact, than would probably have been realized in taxation from private ownership—but that the methods of making such contributions might be improved. One such study was initiated in 1927 for the purpose of appraising the tax situation of the counties in relation to the national forests.[2]

This study showed that in most states the 25 per cent contributions plus federal aid related to the national forests, such as expenditures for roads and law enforcement, approximated or exceeded the potential taxes on these forests. It also revealed the erratic distribution among the counties of both the 25 per cent fund and other benefits.

Another, and more recent, study of this subject was made by the Forest Taxation Inquiry of the Forest Service. A report covering this study was issued January 25, 1937.

This report covers thirty selected counties. The results of this study, also, show total national-forest contributions in excess of potential taxes, and under the heading of "Roads, Fire Protection, and Other Services," is this statement:

"The Federal Government spends large sums annually for the construction and maintenance of roads and trails in and near the National Forests. Part of this money is from the 10 percent of the gross receipts piescribed by Act of March 4, 1913 (37 Stat. 843) and part is from specific appropriations. In the absence of Federal funds, certain of these roads would have been provided for at State and local expense.

"The Federal Government also spends substantial amounts annually protecting the National Forests from fire. A part of this protective effort, in the absence of the national-forest protection system, would have been provided for at State and local expense.

"To some extent law enforcement, game protection, and other services are performed by the national-forest administrative agencies, which services would otherwise be at the expense of State and local government.

---

[2] L. F. Kneipp, "The National Forests as a Form of Federal Aid to the States," 73 Cong., 1 sess., *Sen. Doc. 12,* Separate No. 12. The results of this study are summarized in this part of the Copeland Report, and a more complete report in manuscript is on file.

"The above-mentioned expenditures for roads, fire protection, law enforcement, and the like, which would otherwise have to be carried out at State and local expense, are direct contributions to local government which would not be expected from private owners. Therefore, they may properly be considered as a direct offset to loss of taxes."[3]

The above statement is based upon a comparison, for the thirty counties, between the national-forest contributions to public revenue—the 25 per cent fund and the expenditures for services which would otherwise become the responsibility of state and local government—and the potential tax revenues, state and local, from the national forests. For the three Colorado counties included in this study—Larimer, Mesa, and Mineral—this comparison shows annual contributions from national forests of $68,200 and a potential annual tax revenue of $51,300. For these counties the contributions exceeded the potential tax revenue by about one-third.

A similar comparison, as of the year 1945, for the national forests of Colorado and Wyoming shows results in line with those of the studies quoted above. This comparison is given in the table below for national-forest lands used for grazing and the privately-owned lands classed as range lands for taxation.

A Comparison Between Public Revenue from National-Forest Grazing Lands and Tax Revenue from Privately Owned Grazing Lands

| | National Forest Contributions per Acre | | | | | Average Tax Revenues per Acre | |
	25 per cent fund	Average expenditure for nation-al-forest roads in state	Expenditures for fire control	Total contributions	County levies	Total tax, including county, state, and special levies	
Colorado	1.18 cents	1.71 cents	0.66 cents	3.55 cents	2.94 cents	5.70 cents
Wyoming	1.32 cents	1.40 cents	0.54 cents	3.26 cents	2.84 cents	3.14 cents

[3] *National Forest Contributions to Local Governments,* Forest Taxation Inquiry, Division of Forest Economics, U. S. Forest Service, Washington, D. C.

129

In explanation of the figures given in the above table, the figure for the 25 per cent fund is the 25 per cent of the 1945 grazing fees divided by the net national-forest acreage usable for grazing. The 1945 grazing fee is, of course, considerably above that of the thirties. What the 25 per cent fund will amount to in the future depends upon livestock prices and upon what changes might be made in the national-forest grazing fee base rates.

Expenditures shown in the above table for roads are for those comparable with county and state secondary roads. These figures are for the year 1940, the last year before road expenditures were drastically curtailed by the war. Expenditures for federal highways under the Public Roads Administration are not included in these figures, nor are any of the C.C.C. funds expended in 1940 by the Forest Service for road construction. Both the road and the fire-control expenditures are put on a per acre basis by dividing the net national-forest acreage into the total expenditure for these items in each of the two states. The fire-control expenditure figures are for the year 1945. This expenditure has been about the same each year during the past five years.

The tax figures given in the above table are taken from the Colorado 1943–44 *Yearbook* and from the 1943–44 report of the Wyoming State Board of Equalization. These were the latest reports available at the time the materials in the above table were prepared.

As further comment on the figures in the above table, the "in kind" contributions for roads and fire are only those which would be supported by tax revenue were the lands privately owned. Not included in these figures are the more important local expenditures for the improvement and development of national-forest lands—expenditures which indirectly support the local tax base.

It has been previously mentioned that there appear to be some valid criticisms of the present method of distributing national-forest contributions to the counties. One of these is that since the 25 per cent fund contributions are distributed on the basis of acreage of national-forest lands, there may be inequities due to differences in values and income yields of the national-forest lands. Another is that the 25 per cent fund may fluctuate from year to year because of varying timber sales and the rise and fall of grazing receipts due to changing prices.

From the foregoing information, we see that the problem of loss of tax revenue from the public lands by Western counties is not generally very serious, though there are, no doubt, some exceptions. The annual federal expenditures for the administration and improvement of these public lands offset some, perhaps most, of the loss of tax revenue, and the investment in improvement of the public lands adds something in value to the lands that are in private ownership—the ranch lands especially. Furthermore only a small part of the public lands are really comparable in nature and potential use to the lands now in private ownership and on the tax rolls. We cannot assume that any large acreage of the public lands would support private investment in the needed development and carry the local taxation for the roads and other public improvements.

If the present situation is to be changed by federal legislation to remunerate local government for loss of tax revenue by paying a percentage of the appraised value of federal public lands to such local government, the appraisal should recognize at the outset that the valuation procedures and the value concepts must be entirely different from those evolved in private land taxation. The lands are not comparable in character and use, nor are the tax-revenue requirements for the public lands comparable with tax revenue needs for private lands. Furthermore, the federal administration would likely continue to carry much of the public-service cost on the public lands, even though a full tax equivalent on those lands were paid to the states and counties.

This proposal for payment on an appraised value has merit, however, as a substitute for the present policy patchwork. It may be desirable, if well conceived and administered, as a measure to replace the several present methods and rates for annual payments to counties of some share of the revenue from the use of the public lands. The appraisal of the capital values of the public lands should be a conservative figure based on only the commercial values of these lands. The annual payment should not exceed three-fourths of 1 per cent of the appraised capital value of the land.

Underpricing and Overgrazing of the Public Lands

In a free market, price balances supply and demand. This axiom of economics has been denied in pricing the grazing use of the Western public lands. The consequence of a low price has been excessive demand for and overuse of this grazing, overcapitalization of the grazing privileges and of the ranch properties, poorly equalized taxation, and unfair competition for the ranches on private range land.

When the present Western national-forest lands were withdrawn from the public domain, many of them were used as free grazing. Soon after they were withdrawn, a small charge was placed upon the grazing for those permitted to continue this use. Subsequent proposed increases in the charge for grazing met such opposition that an appraisal study was made, during the nineteen twenties, of the national-forest grazing. The findings of this study were compromised, and the result is a charge that, over a series of years from high to low live-stock prices, averages about fifteen cents per animal month for cattle and five cents for sheep. These prices, which are varied in relation to livestock prices, average less than one-half of market values.

When administration of the public-domain lands was started under the Taylor Act of 1934, the grazing charge was initiated at five cents a head per month for cattle and one cent a month for sheep. These charges excluded animals under six months of age, which were grazed free. When these lands were used as open range, they were used without charge. Recently these charges have been increased to eight cents for cattle, and one and three-fifths cents for sheep. One-fourth of this fee goes to the grazing districts for range improvements. These fees from the grazing districts probably amount to about 40 per cent of the average value of this grazing over a series of years. This is on terms of our past concepts of the general price level.

Attempts by the federal administrative agencies to push these charges for grazing upward toward commercial levels have met continued strong political resistance from the Western livestock industry organizations. Such resistance comes especially from larger permittees. They do not wish to yield their advantage of low-cost grazing, but, more important and more significant, they do not want the added administration and controls that likely will come with the increased charges. For Congress has been reluctant to increase the appropriations toward adequate levels for Western public-land administration without concomitant increases in the revenues from these lands.

A perusal of the hearings of the Congressional committees concerning the proposals for public-land grazing charges reveals a repetition of the following statements by those who oppose higher fees:

(1) The national forests have a low commercial grazing value because of their remoteness from ranches and the resulting high cost of using this grazing, because of losses from poison plants and predators, and because the forest regulations prevent speculative profits from increasing and decreasing livestock numbers.

(2) The public-domain grazing has little commercial value because these lands have low grazing capacity and are winter "maintenance ranges."

(3) Most of the annual cycle of feed and forage comes from the private lands; the public lands are a necessary accessory for the ranches but are supplementary, most of the investment and the cost necessarily being in the ranch properties.

There is, of course, some basis for all of these statements. However, the most cogent argument against now raising the public-land grazing fees to a commercial level is that the long delay in such action has caused the differential between the charge for, and the value of, public-land grazing to appear in the capital values of the ranch properties. Thus, with the sale of ranches at prices including this capital value, this differential has its effect upon debt and taxation structures.

We lack any good measure of the actual influence of this capitalization upon ranch property values and tax rates. We can, however, make some fairly accurate deductions concerning the situations where the influence is most important. It is most important where the public-land use is a major part of the total land use, where there is no necessity for developing expensive ranch property, and where there is little or no alternative for the ranches but to use the public lands as a part of the balanced year-round ranch operation. We see this situation especially in the yearlong ranges of the public-domain lands in the Southwest and in parts of Nevada and Utah.

So far as public policy is concerned, the most impelling reason for raising the public-land grazing fees to a commercial level is to balance demand with supply. Public-land administrative agencies now face constant pressure for increased grazing permits and—what is more important—pressure against the reductions in grazing use needed to conserve the resource. And the overuse which makes these reductions necessary was engendered by a price that did not balance supply and demand.

Another good reason for raising public-land grazing fees is the adverse effect, in most public-land communities, of the low fees upon the substantial number of ranches that do not have any public-land grazing. These ranches that do not have the benefit of low-cost public-land grazing find their local taxes influenced upward by the higher capitalization of the private lands of those ranches that do have public-land grazing permits. Beyond this effect, those ranches without the public-land use are at a disadvantage in competing with the subsidized ranches for the leasing of private lands. In other words, those ranches without the public-land permits cannot use them to "average down" total land cost.

Why, it may be asked, is not the answer to this question of pricing the public-land grazing to be had in letting that use through competitive bid? But that would probably result in high bid for speculative use in years of high prices, little or no use of the lands during years of low prices, and consequent instability for the ranch operations and the local communities. For illustration, in 1945 some sizable units of range land of the Crow Indian Reservation in Montana were leased for a five-year term at a price of over fifteen dollars per head, annually, for cattle grazing. This was a competitive-bid lease in a period of price inflation. Even for yearlong grazing use—and it probably is nearly so—the price is speculative and far beyond normal value standards.

In summary, it seems desirable that the grazing use of all public lands be priced at or near the commercial value of that use. In attaining that policy, some loss will accrue to the owners of ranch property with any considerable capitalization of the differential between the prices and values of the public-land grazing permits. But those losses will likely be far less important than the gains, both individual and social, from a price that balances supply and demand.

V. Livestock Grazing and Land Use

The Western Range Industry

WEST OF THE HUNDREDTH MERIDIAN the landscape seems more expansive. On this spacious land we observe the occasional ranch dwelling, the canvas-topped sheep wagon on a distant hill, and the indolent group of beef cattle, statuelike in a valley. To many who see this from the highways or from the picture windows of the streamliners, "ranch country" means this and little more. There are those who question the importance of this feature of our Western and national economy.

However, probably something like one-third of the nation's beef cattle and two-thirds of the sheep are maintained on the ranches and stock farms of the West, and these animals inhabit, for some part of the year, those spacious ranges that seem from the highways to be nearly devoid of life. Now, let us note that these Western range livestock populations are, in the main, breeding herds. Most of the range cattle are cows, now, where formerly the steers were retained to maturity. Most of the range sheep are now breeding ewes, where formerly great bands of wether sheep were maintained primarily for their wool. Annually the calf crop and the lamb crop of the Western ranches now move eastward to the feed lots and pastures of the corn-belt farms. Western range livestock production now has a high economic integration with the farms of the corn belt and of the Western irrigated districts.

Let us now look at some of the contrasts in the Western ranch country and in the ranching. At least half, perhaps more, of the Western range livestock production is in the western Great Plains. In the immense and productive northern, central and southern regions of the plains we see some sharp contrasts in the range industry and in the ranches. We see a fifteen-million-acre cowman's domain in the Nebraska Sand Hills; we see an even larger shepherd's empire in the Edwards Plateau of Texas. In the Central Plains, much of the stock-ranch production depends upon a combination of native grassland with wheat pasturages and grain-sorghum feeds. Southern Plains range grazing is yearlong; that of the Northern Plains requires from two to three months of winter feeding of hay and other crop feeds. From all the plains ranches and stock farms, in the fall, countless trainloads of feeder calves and lambs roll eastward to the corn-belt farm feed lots.

As we turn our eyes westward now to the ranch country of the Rocky Mountains, we see an entirely different set of natural operating factors. Ranches are located in the mountain valleys, where they can grow the irrigated feed crops that they must feed through the three to five months' winter season. Ranges are seasonal, requiring some trail movement of the livestock, especially for sheep. High mountain ranges are usable only as summer range; foothills provide the spring and fall range. Cattle ranches on high foothill land have green pastures through the six to eight months' range season. In contrast with the plains ranches, these ranches market quite a percentage of slaughter animals—range-fattened lambs and grass-fattened steers.

West of the Rocky Mountains, and reaching to the Sierras and the Cascades, is a new and different kind of ranch country and ranching. In this Intermountain region, we have to revise our concept of what constitutes a sheep ranch, for it seems that the range bands are always on the move. Excepting the early-lambing sheep ranches in the Snake River Valley of southern Idaho and eastern Oregon, the range bands of sheep are grazed year-round in a cycle of migration to seasonal ranges. Desert lands constitute the winter range, mountain lands the summer range, and the intervening sagebrush lands the spring and fall range.

137

California Central Valley range lands and ranches provide the extreme in contrast with other regions. From November through May the annual grasses of these ranges of the Sierra foothills and of the coastal mountains are lush and green. During the hot and rainless summer, the range feed is harsh, dry, and poor, and the livestock require supplemental feed to maintain their weight. Cattle ranches adapt their operations to these natural conditions by buying stocker cattle in the autumn, marketing in April and May, and feeding the breeding herd a range supplement through the summer. These ranches are productive, and their capitalization is high. They enjoy a price advantage because of the large California market and the heavy California in-shipment of beef.

We look, finally, at the ranch country of the Southwest, from the Pecos River in Texas west to the Gila drainage in Arizona. Again, we have to make a shift in our thinking about what ranches are and how they operate. Rainfall has two distinct seasonal "humps" in this land of *poco llueve*—in July and August, and again in February and March. The late summer rains make the feed on the grama grasslands; the later winter rains—if they come in volume—make the desert lands bloom with the annuals. Most of the ranches operate in the grama grassland areas. Use of the desert range is highly speculative.

Although we see many contrasts in the range industry and in the ranches, we see one important similarity in all the many different types of Western range livestock production. That is the harvesting by range livestock of range forage from large expanses of land that, by farm-pasture standards, are low-grade resources. Yet the Western range industry greatly enhances our Western and national economy. This industry depends upon a resource that is eminently worth conserving and that should receive a greater share of the efforts of agricultural science and of land-conservation work.

Public Lands and the Western Range Industry

IT IS ESTIMATED THAT, as of 1945, the range and pasture grazing by the beef cattle and sheep population of the eleven Western states totaled some 118,282,000 animal-unit months—one cow month or five sheep months equaling one animal-unit month. This calculation assumes, as an average, ten months on range and pasture for stock sheep and eight months on range and pasture for beef cattle. In these eleven states that contain most of the Western public lands, public-land grazing supplied some 36,841,000 animal-unit months of grazing, or 31 per cent of the estimated total range and pasture grazing. In the table below is shown the animal-unit months of grazing on the different kinds of western federal public land:

Western Public-Land Grazing as of 1945

Kind of Public Land	Animal-Unit Months of Grazing
Public domain (grazing districts)	15,000,000
National forests	10,466,000
Indian reservations	7,500,000
Public domain (general land office)	2,225,000
L–U project lands	1,650,000
Total	36,841,000

For interpretation of the above calculations, it should be emphasized that they are only for the eleven Western states and, consequently, do not cover the entire Western range industry. The important ranges of Texas, the Dakotas, Oklahoma, and Nebraska are not included because our analysis concerns federal public lands and these states do not have any important grazing use of such lands. Thus, if we were to compare the total of Western public-land grazing to the total range use of the entire Western range industry, the relative importance of the

139

public lands would be considerably less than the 31 per cent figure given above.

We should note further that this percentage figure for the eleven Western states is a comparison for range and pasture lands only. Inclusion in the range and pasture use total of the animal months of range livestock maintenance on harvested crops and crop aftermath would show that public-land grazing supplied 22 per cent of the total maintenance for the beef cattle and the stock sheep of the eleven Western states.

For further interpretation of these calculations concerning the relationship of public-land grazing to the Western range industry, we should note that a rather large percentage of the beef-cattle and stock-sheep populations of the eleven Western states are farm-beef herds and farm-flock sheep that are grazed on farm pastures rather than on range. Thus, for the stock ranches that use range-land grazing, the public-land grazing is a great deal more than the 31 per cent of their total range use. An analysis of census data showing the size characteristics of the livestock enterprises of the eleven Western states indicates that probably the farm-flock sheep enterprises account for 20 to 25 per cent of the stock-sheep numbers of these states, and that the farm herds of beef cattle may total almost half of the beef-cattle population. It seems a good guess that, in the eleven Western states, the public lands supply at least 40 per cent of the range-land grazing for the beef-cattle and sheep enterprises that are truly range enterprises.

In this analysis of the relationship of public-land grazing to the range livestock enterprises of the eleven Western states, we should note, further, that to a large extent both the public lands and the privately owned range lands of the ranches that use the public lands are highly seasonal in their adapted grazing use, and that they are complementary in effecting a well-balanced year-round livestock capacity for the ranches. This seasonal aspect of public-land grazing is illustrated by the fact that national-forest grazing is limited to the summer season, except in

140

some of the Southwestern national forests. Public-domain grazing is largely winter grazing on the desert lands, and spring and fall grazing on most of the other range types. There is a great deal of summer grazing and some yearlong grazing on the public domain in some localities. Grazing on the Indian reservations is season-long for the Indian-owned stock, which is now near three-fourths of the total grazed on the reservations, but is more or less seasonal for other stock.

We can see the economic importance, for the livestock enterprises that use the public lands, of the seasonal nature of the public-land grazing and the interdependence in the use of private and public lands. Many ranches that use public lands could, with varying degrees of success, reorganize their livestock enterprises and use of land to operate without the use of the public lands. For the ranches that could effect such a reorganization, the reduction in the livestock numbers would usually be greater, proportionately, than the reduction in total land use due to loss of the public-land use. Some ranches with highly seasonal privately owned lands that can be used only jointly with seasonal public-land grazing could not effect any workable reorganization to operate without the public-land grazing.

We see from the foregoing that the grazing use of the public lands is important in the livestock economy of the eleven Western public-land states, and is especially important in the range livestock economy of these states. Grazing use of the public lands is substantially less for the total Western range economy than for that of the eleven Western states only. Nationally, the public-land range use is a minor part of the total forage and feed requirement of the beef cattle and sheep population. Public-land grazing, as of 1945, provided around 5 per cent, nationally, of the total animal months of forage and feed for beef cattle and stock sheep.

141

TENANCY AND LAND TENURE FOR
WESTERN STOCK RANCHES

TENANT OPERATORS AND SHARECROPPERS are un-
known, or nearly so, in Western stock ranching. Most Western
stock-ranch operators own at least part of the land they use. For
certain types or ranches, full operator ownership is the rule; for
others, the lands owned are mainly those that afford the best
competitive base for the leasing of other lands.

Why do we see so little tenant operation of Western stock
ranches? Probably most important among the reasons are the
high capital requirement for stocking a ranch and the reluctance
of an owner to turn the management of livestock over to a sharecropper. Important, also, in this lack of tenant operation of
ranches is the size of the enterprise of Western ranches. Although there are many small ranches, stocked with one hundred
head of cattle or less, even these are sizable in terms of the investment required of a tenant operator. Of some importance,
also, is the usual practice of the Western public-land administrative agencies to require operator ownership of the ranch base
property as a qualification for a public-land grazing permit. This
base property is, in the northern regions, feed-crop land, though
it may also be seasonal range lands of critical supply that are
needed to balance the seasonal use of the public land. In the
southern regions the base property may be range land with water
development, or seasonal range especially needed to make a good
year-round balance with the seasonal grazing of the public land.

Although we seldom see a ranch operated by a tenant or by
a sharecropper, many ranches, probably a high percentage of
the total, lease some land or make some use of the public lands.
Ranch surveys of the past in the Northern Plains have shown
that the ranches of this region leased, on an average, about half
of the range land that they used. Leased lands were railroad
grant lands, state lands, county tax default lands, foreclosed
lands held by credit agencies, and absentee-owned homesteads.

Probably the ranches of the Central and Southern Plains regions own a higher percentage of the lands used than do those of the Northern Plains.

Ranches of the Rocky Mountain foothills tend to full ownership of their land. Especially is this true of the cattle ranches, for they can often use this type of land through the full range season. Cattle and sheep ranches of the Rocky Mountain region that have summer range permits on the national forests own their irrigated meadow and other feed-crop lands, and own or lease foothill land for spring and fall range.

In the Intermountain and Southwestern regions, where the public domain, the national forests, and the state lands all are of considerable importance to the ranches, the deeded lands of the ranches are at a minimum as a percentage of the total land used. In these regions the ranches characteristically own only those feed-crop lands, range lands with water, or critical seasonal range lands that are most strategic in controlling leases and gaining public-land range permits. Sheep ranch operations having a winter range on the public-domain desert lands and a summer range permit on the national forests usually own some range land suitable for the intervening spring and fall grazing. For the Intermountain region, this range-land ownership is, as a rule, in the sagebrush zone, or elevational limits. In the Southwestern region, the ranch-property base may be only a tract for the buildings and the water development. There are, however, areas in this region where most of the land is deeded. The productive grama grasslands of southeastern Arizona and southwestern New Mexico are one illustration of this.

Ranches of the California Central Valley characteristically own a major part of their land. These ranches have the highest rate of capitalization of range lands per unit of grazing use of all Western ranches, with the possible exception of some of the Texas range areas.

Thus we see that, at least to the present time, the economy of the Western stock ranches has not been conducive to the development of ranch tenancy and sharecropping systems comparable with those of corn-belt or cotton-belt farms. Much of the land used by the ranches is leased land or public land, but the leasing and permits are, as a rule, dependent upon ownership of the kind of land most essential as the base property.

WHAT IS HAPPENING TO THE FAMILY-TYPE STOCK RANCH?

ONE POPULAR MISCONCEPTION about Western ranch economy is that large pioneer ranches are gradually and eventually shaping into a pattern of family-type holdings and communities of ranch homes. That is not a true picture, and today there are new and seemingly unpredictable factors that will influence present types of ranch ownership.

First, as a background for an analysis of the present situation and the trends in types of ranch ownership, let us attempt to define and describe the family-type stock ranch. It is necessary to define this type of ranch, first, in terms of size that will provide a family income. The relationship of size to outlet for family labor is secondary. This is true because of the usual isolation of the ranch family and the consequent higher cash requirement for a living comparable with that of the family in farming communities. A net cash income for family use of three thousand dollars annually is a minimum for the ranch family, and this means, under normal prices and costs, a ranch operation of three hundred head of cattle or two thousand ewes. We can place the upper limit in size for the family-type stock ranch at the point necessary to get full advantage of ranch economy and management. In most situations this is around five hundred head of cattle and four thousand ewes.

A large number of the Western stock ranches come within this definition of size for the family ranch. They are, however, in the minority, both in numbers and in land acreage operated. In the general Western picture these family-type ranches are

144

probably exceeded in acreage and in production by the larger ranches, in ownership other than that of the family living on and operating the ranch. Here the important distinction is that these larger ranches are essentially investments and are so regarded and operated, even though the management may be that of a resident and noncorporate owner.

In numbers, though not in production, the family-size ranches are exceeded by the small ranches and stock farms of subeconomic size. Any ranch that operates less than one hundred head of cattle or less than a full range band of sheep may be classed as subeconomic. For, as a rule, the stock ranch has scant possibility for intensification and diversification or for substitution of home products for family income. Small ranches do not afford an outlet for family labor. Usually these subeconomic ranch units have little chance to compete and little opportunity to grow. Most of them result from either an attempt to develop homestead farms into ranches or an effort by a ranch employee to start with a small herd of cattle on a small owned-land base. These small operations are on the wane. Most of them are a hopeless struggle for the operator.

A study of Western stock ranching soon convinces one that the stock ranch is, of necessity, a commercial enterprise and that management know-how is more necessary for the family ranch than for the family farm. Seldom can the ranch diversify and spread its risk. Its income is highly seasonal. The capital requirements for land and livestock are high. Management has to be good.

Western stock-ranch economy is yet somewhat immature, and there are several factors, some of them recent, that work against the continuation of family-type ranches and make their future uncertain. For one thing, the "agricultural ladder" that has worked reasonably well in most farming areas, works scarcely at all with the stock ranches. Ranches are almost never leased on shares by an owner. He seldom wants to turn livestock over to tenant management. And the capital requirements for the livestock to stock a ranch are usually too high for a tenant. Ranch lands are usually a combination of deeded and leased lands, the deeded land and water giving the key to leasing private lands and grazing on seasonal public ranges in a balanced year-round operation. This is the situation that made possible the growth of the pioneer ranches without a large investment in land. And as a consequence of this interdependence of the use of crop land, water, and seasonal range lands, it is not possible to lease a tract of range and start a ranch as a farmer might lease an "eighty" to start farming. Moreover, the key tracts of the private lands are nearly all held by present ranch ownerships.

Land-capital requirements have been considerably increased in recent years by the competitive purchase, by ranches, of range lands formerly leased as a part of the ranches. High capitalization of the public-land grazing permits in the sale of the ranches has also added materially in recent years to the capital requirements of many of the stock ranches in the eleven Western states. All of these things appear to be obstacles to the continuation and regeneration of the family-type ranch ownership. Yet another factor has been the purchase of ranches by those outside the industry with war-generated investment money. This has been a real factor in the inflation of ranch values, and its eventual effect in determining type of ranch ownership is difficult to appraise.

Thus we can see that while many large pioneer ranches have been divided into family-type operations, there now appear to be some strong influences toward large investment holdings of ranch property—away from the type of ranch which the operator and family own, live upon, and use for their job and their livelihood. One consequence of this tendency is a loss in good land use.

This loss is due to the fact that the large investment holdings are semispeculative and there is not the same attitude toward the resource as that of the owner-operator. This corporate operation, in seeking dividends for shareholders, is more apt to mine the resource. And at the other extreme of the scale, the small, subeconomic ranches are the most persistent and severe overusers and mismanagers of Western grazing lands.

If the family-type Western stock ranch gives best land use, as well as other social values, what can be done to aid the succession and regeneration of that type of ranch? Probably not much that would be advisable, now, until the present overcapitalization situation has settled and the consequence of investment purchasing of ranches has been clarified. But when that time comes—probably within the next five years—there may be opportunity, both through private financial agencies and through government policy, to strengthen the economic viability of the family-type stock ranch.

This may be accomplished through careful analysis of large ranches, as they come into the sale market, for the possibility of subdividing them into natural land units and well-balanced ranch-management units of economic family-type size. Where this can be done, the ranch will have a higher sound value than as one unit. Not all large ranches have this possibility; some of them are large natural units. But most of the original large ranch units do have some such possibility, as will most of the recent investment ranches when they come back into a deflated sale market.

RANCHES, BALANCED AND UNBALANCED

A GOOD BALANCE among the various seasonal rangeland and feed-crop capacities is now the first requisite in the management of the Western stock ranch. It is the basic management requirement.

In most ranching localities this feature of ranch management concerns the management of range land, for the development of crop feeds is now usually adequate to balance the capacity of the range lands. In fact, the crop feeds now, more often than not, overbalance the capacity of the range lands. It is, consequently, the objective of good ranch managers to have a well-balanced relationship between the various seasonal feed and forage components that make for a year-round capacity, without any seasonal gaps or pressure points. For some ranches this relationship involves the summer range, the spring-fall range, and the meadow hay and pasturage for winter. For other ranches the balance is between a season-long range and the feed crops. For the ranches that use the same range yearlong, the attainment of a good seasonal balance may be in the management of the range so that the cool-weather and the warm-weather forage plants grow in a good range-forage capacity relationship.

Ranch appraisers who do appraisal and management-analysis work for land-credit institutions say that, more often than not, Western stock ranches are not well-balanced in their feed and forage capacities. Among the unbalanced ranches are those having a local-resource situation that causes a natural lack of balance, as the old cowman says, "because of the way the country is put together." Probably most of the unbalanced ranches are, however, the result of some unfavorable trend in one or more of their seasonal ranges, of an excess or deficit of crop feeds, or of a lack of good planning in the acquiring or leasing of the right types of land in the amounts needed for a well-balanced unit. Let us look at a few typical examples of well-balanced and unbalanced ranches.

First let us look at a ranch in the Northern Plains, near Sundance, Wyoming. This ranch must depend on native hay for the winter feed, and by spreading the spring runoff onto valley bottom land, it has produced and stored adequate feed. In the fencing plan for this ranch, the range is separated into four pastures, and each year the use of one of these pastures is deferred in a plan of rotation until July 1, or thereabouts. As a consequence, it has been possible to hold a good range-forage growth relationship between the mid-grasses that provide the early-season and late-season feed, and the short grasses that provide the summer grazing. As the result of good management, this

Grazing on the subalpine watershed lands must be moderate and well managed to prevent destruction of the native plants and mountain topsoil, nature's blotter for "walking" the water downhill

ranch is well-balanced and the range-plant and soil resources are unimpaired.

In the Sweet Grass Valley of south-central Montana, east of the Crazy Mountains and just north of the Yellowstone, is a ranch fairly typical of the Northern Rocky Mountain valley and foothill ranches. This ranch produces irrigated alfalfa hay for the rather long feeding period, and grazes through the range season, from early May to early November, on foothill bunch-grass range. But this ranch, like many others of the Sweet Grass and near-by Boulder valleys, has overused the range because of the ease with which irrigated hay acreage could be increased to feed more livestock through the winter. As a consequence of the down trend in the grazing capacity of the overused range and the increase in the irrigated alfalfa acreage, these valleys are now known locally as "hay-surplus areas." But this surplus is due in part to the lowered range-land capacity, and the fact that this and other ranches of the Sweet Grass are now unbalanced is due both to overexpansion of hay acreage and to overuse of the range.

Near Fort Huachucha, in southeastern Arizona, is a ranch located in beautiful rolling hills covered with the southwestern mixed grama range type. Grazing on this range is yearlong. Through carefully conservative use of the range and by seasonal rotation of the use of different parts of the range, the management of this range has been able to maintain the natural complement of palatable shrubs and weeds. These shrubs furnish some winter grazing, and the weeds some early spring forage. Without these plants the range would not be well balanced seasonally, for as a pure grama grassland this range would fluctuate much more in its grazing capacity between the favorable and the unfavorable years. Not a few owners of this range type have learned about this the hard way and to their economic disadvantage.

Through these illustrations, we see that, in addition to the long-time essential objective of resource maintenance, good ranch management seeks to attain a well-balanced ranch unit for the greater profits that result—usually over a short period, and certainly over a long period of time.

RECENT TRENDS IN WESTERN STOCK RANCHING

SEVERAL distinct, widespread, and noteworthy trends are discernible in the economy of Western stock ranches. Some favorable trends appear to be countered by those that are unfavorable. Let us undertake to appraise these trends, with special reference to the good use and maintenance of the resources upon which the Western stock-ranching operations depend.

Most important of all is the widespread down trend in the range resource. Lack of recognition and lack of awareness of this trend and of its significance appear to be general. This is not strange. Some countervailing factors have offset and obscured the economic effects of this down trend. Greater use of improved pastures, greater use of crop feeds, increased use of high-protein range supplements, improved and better-adapted breeds and types of livestock—all of these have countered the economic effects of the range deterioration. There are those who deny the existence of any widespread impairment in the range resource. They cite "good" illustrations for proof. The illustrations are localized, are due to a recent favorable climatic situation, or are otherwise defective. Good managers among the ranch operators know that we are faced with this general deterioration of the range resource.

Some rather recent developments in breeds and types of livestock are a good omen for better future use of Western range lands. Blocky and low-set cattle and large whiteface-crossbred sheep have demonstrated their efficiency, if given favorable pasture and feed conditions. Although these breeds and types do not thrive on low-grade or rough and poorly watered range, they are easily competitively superior, on good forage and feed, to types of animals better able to use rough, low-capacity ranges.

150

It seems likely that we shall see more of these superior animals on good pastures, on fenced and improved ranges, and on range land that is susceptible of cultural treatment and management. If this trend develops rapidly, as seems probable, we shall in time see the low-grade ranges—the depleted ranges that are difficult to manage and difficult to restore—slip below the competitive-use margin. Perhaps the time is not far distant when many such range lands simply will not be used. Increased production from the better lands may cause great acreages of range lands now used to become submarginal for range-livestock production.

Yet another consequence of the recent and rather startling development in breeds and types of animals for use on Western stock ranches is the greater economic integration of the economy of the Western ranches and the economy of the corn-belt farms. These new types of cattle make better, earlier-maturing, and more efficient young feeder animals, and they lose much of this efficiency if retained on the ranges past the yearling stage or if held on the range to make grass beef. The ranches are, consequently, turning to a breeding-herd operation, increasing their calf crops by better herd management, and greatly increasing the ratio of annual marketings to the numbers of animals maintained on the range. Once this ratio was 20 to 30 per cent; now it is 45 or 50 per cent. Thus the efficiency of the entire production cycle, from the range through the feed lot, is increasing. There will yet be some "hatrack" cattle marketed from Western ranges, but the markets will be increasingly unreceptive.

Let us note briefly some other significant trends in Western ranching.

Western stock ranches have become larger during the past two or three decades; they now own more land and lease less, so that the capital requirements are higher for ranch ownership. Then, in the past decade we have seen a tremendous rise in the capitalization of ranch properties, per head of ranch capacity for livestock. Ranches now sell at one hundred to two hundred dollars per head of capacity for cattle, whereas our past concept of normal value is about one-half these figures. This high capitalization has been further accentuated in some localities by an inflated concept of the numbers of livestock that ranches will carry. Especially is this true in the Northern Plains, where, because of nearly a decade of exceptionally favorable years, ranches are now selling on a basis of fifteen to twenty acres of land per cow, but a long-time safe figure is at least thirty acres per cow.

This excessive capitalization of Western ranches is inimical to good land use. We are almost certain to see, within a decade, the land misuse and financial aftermath of this recent trend of ranch prices. Probably the trend toward larger ranches is not unfavorable to good land use, except where there have been consolidations and speculative purchases or where the lands are otherwise not strongly held.

VI. Reclamation, Whither Bound?

RECLAMATION, HOW MUCH AND HOW SOON?

THERE ARE in the arid Western states the irrigable lands and the water resources to approximately double the some twenty million acres of Western irrigation that we had in 1940. How rapidly should we develop this agricultural resource?

This question of the rate at which we should develop this additional acreage of irrigated land through federal reclamation is essentially a question of how soon we should have the Western hydroelectric power and the related industrial development that these reclamation projects can provide. For it is such development that accelerates economic opportunity for industry and population growth. And this, in turn, enhances the economics of the Western irrigated agriculture.

Our increasing West Coast population already is causing some regional food deficits. Deficits in the bulky foods necessitating the longer rail haul, as the deficit zone extends eastward, increases the market prices to the Western food growers. As the Western population increases, this may be an appreciable influence favorable to the competitive economics of Western irrigated agriculture.

But, even more important in this future irrigation development, hydroelectric power can carry a large share of the cost of Western reclamation projects—if we permit such power to be developed—and can give the needed basis for Western industrial expansion. To a large extent, the small, low-cost irrigation enterprise have already been developed. Most of these developments have been private. In the large multipurpose projects now built and planned as federal reclamation developments, irrigation becomes almost a by-product. As of March, 1947, hydroelectric power was scheduled to repay nearly three-fourths of the total cost of all reclamation projects.

All this may sound somewhat like a national investment in Western regional industrial development—a planned influence upon relative regional growth rates. Probably to some extent it is. We shall see as a consequence of the Western reclamation projects a somewhat greater and more rapid industrial dispersion, nationally. The investment appears to be a good one, both fiscally and in terms of national economic policy.

One may question the degree to which Western industrial expansion must depend upon further development of hydroelectric power. In 1943, six of the eleven Western states depended upon hydroelectric power for 95 per cent or more of their total electric power. California's total electric power was nearly three-fourths hydroelectric. It is true that since 1943 the rising power requirements of these states have caused them to turn more to other generating sources—mainly higher-cost sources than the additional hydroelectric capacity that could be developed.

This potential increase in our national agricultural production that would result from a doubling of the Western irrigated land acreage is of sufficient magnitude to be considered in relation to the national agricultural production and needs. It now appears likely that, for a time, we shall have surplus agricultural production capacity, though there are some unknowns in that. These unknowns—the trend of international affairs, the rate of our own population growth, our level of national employment and income, and the rate at which we are destroying land or making it submarginal—are such that it may be the wiser national policy to plan for agricultural surpluses rather than scarcities. It appears especially important to consider that the new irrigated lands of the West may replace lands that are becoming submarginal in the older agricultural areas, and that the added irrigation may not more than meet the increased needs of a rapidly growing Western population for meats, dairy products, and certain other foods.

154

Another feature of national policy that enters into this question of Western reclamation expansion is the unbalance that appears to be developing in the Western population. Although there is a continued surge of migration to the Pacific states, it seems probable that the thinly peopled lands between the hundredth meridian and the Sierras and Cascades may lose population. For these lands are essentially agricultural and we shall have a smaller national rural population as advances continue in agricultural technology. One way, and perhaps the only way, to offset the tendency for this part of the West to become a forgotten hinterland is to develop the full potentialities of hydroelectric power from the reclamation developments. That will not stop the loss of rural population, but will offset it by making industrial and urban growth possible. Should this large area of the Western states have a declining population and a shrinking economy during the next two decades, it would be a weak spot in the fabric of our national life.

Perhaps we now plan to develop Western reclamation too rapidly. There are, for example, those planners who would have the multibillion Missouri Valley development plan completed in the coming six years. Aside from questions of national security and the urgency that may stem therefrom, this seems too short a time. Those who have studied Western reclamation for many years say that we now plan to do in five or ten years what would be much better planned and done in twenty to thirty years.

Reclamation Reaches Out

Twenty years ago the Bureau of Reclamation of the Department of the Interior was essentially an engineering agency. Now the agricultural- and power-resource planning, development, and management activities of this agency overshadow its engineering work. This change, with the rapid expansion of the reclamation program, is highly significant.

For, with the development of the large multipurpose recla-

155

mation projects, the control and administration of such projects carries a large measure of authority in the planning and directing of the economy of an entire region. Policies for the use of the water and the power from a project such as the Grand Coulee may be a dominant force in the development of an entire river basin. And within the past few years, hydroelectric power has become the key to Western irrigation reclamation. Any doubts concerning that will be dispelled by a look at the statistics.

The some three hundred contracts in effect between the water users' organizations and the Secretary of the Interior in March, 1947, call for $352,400,000 to be paid by irrigation water users, $546,190,000 to be paid by power revenues on the power investment, and an additional $473,315,000 to be paid by power on the irrigation investment. Power revenues are to repay over $1,000,000,000 out of the total of $1,372,000,000 of the reimbursable costs of the reclamation projects, as of 1947. A substantial part of the cost of the large multipurpose projects is sometimes a nonreimbursable federal government investment for flood control or for other public benefit. The Garrison Dam on the Missouri is an example of this.

Federal reclamation projects now account for approximately two million acres of the twenty million acres of irrigated land in the Western states. In addition, the federal reclamation projects supply some supplemental water for about two million acres of privately developed irrigated land. But the federal reclamation projects now under construction or authorized for construction will add ten million acres to the irrigation development. And the ultimate plans for reclamation call for a total of some twenty million acres of such development—a doubling of the acreage of irrigated lands in the Western states as reported by the 1940 census.

In September, 1947, the construction program of the Bureau of Reclamation for the fiscal year 1948 added up to a total of approximately two hundred million dollars. This did not include the contributions made to the reclamation projects as flood-con-

Colorado Agricultural and Mechanical College

Western irrigated agriculture produces a large proportion of many of our specialty crops

trol work, under the flood-control act of 1944. The total reclamation expenditure for the fiscal year 1948 dwarfs the reclamation operations of fifteen years ago. This figure is in turn dwarfed by the reclamation plans for the future. Completion of the California Central Valley reclamation development, it is estimated, will cost something over a billion dollars. The Central Arizona development plan, which has recently received Bureau of Reclamation approval though it has not yet received Congressional authorization, would cost about three-quarters of a billion dollars. Completion of the Bureau of Reclamation and Army Corps of Engineers "Pick-Sloan Plan" for Missouri basin development calls for an expenditure, during the next few years, of three to six billion dollars.

This Missouri development, when complete, will store one hundred million acre-feet of water, and it may in time add several million new acres—perhaps as many as five million—to Western irrigated lands. Most of this irrigation development will be in the plains. When one looks at a map of this proposed irrigation for the Missouri Valley, he is impelled to the thought: the planning for this development will shape the future economy of the Northern Plains, from the Republican River to the Souris River.

With this rather startling increase in the size and scope of Bureau of Reclamation operations, there has been, just in recent years, a parallel expansion in the size of the Bureau of Reclamation staff and a diversification of the talents of this staff. In the Western regional and project offices of this bureau there is now a large staff of agricultural technicians, extension workers, project and farm planners, and resource and social policy analysts and planners.

Only a few years ago the Bureau of Reclamation was justifiably criticized for being almost oblivious to all except the engineering features of reclamation project planning and development, but now the criticism runs in the other direction. It is now said, with a great deal of justification, that the greatly expanded

157

agricultural organization of this bureau goes far beyond the advisory needs for reclamation project planning and development and that it now duplicates much of the work of the Department of Agriculture, the land-grant colleges, and the state agricultural extension services.

This expanded agricultural work, resource planning, and policy analysis may be only a part of the organizational plans which some have for the Bureau of Reclamation. Such plans for the eventual organization of reclamation work may encompass a pattern of Western regional services, or "valley authorities," for the co-ordinated planning and development of resources, power, industry—in fact, of the whole economy—of a river basin or a region.

Perhaps we may, in the future, desire such regional or river-basin organization and provide for it through suitable legislation. We may now be moving toward such planning and administration, without either the necessary legislation or the administrative design for such development of our economy.

RECLAMATION SOCIAL POLICY

SOCIAL-POLICY FEATURES OF Western reclamation development had their inception in the Reclamation Act of 1902. That act limited the size of the farms on federal reclamation projects to 160 acres. This was a logical provision, since the act authorized the use of interest-free money to prepare the public domain for homesteading. Perhaps it may be said that the main purpose of this act was to extend our Western settlement frontier.

Now, with reclamation operations affecting largely the lands that are in private ownership, we have a new set of social-policy questions and issues, additional to those concerning public-land reclamation. For one thing, size limitation has quite a different meaning when applied to lands in private ownership. Some of these may be held in large acreages, and the excess may have to be sold to the government at an appraised price or disposed

158

of otherwise. Then, the use of interest-free money and the length of the repayment contract have different significance when applied to private lands. Other questions of social and economic policy that have arisen in recent years are the retention by government of title to the water supplies developed for Bureau of Reclamation projects; the subsidizing of irrigation through power revenues; the payment of interest on the power investment; the term of years for the irrigation repayment contracts; and the prior authorization of projects by the Bureau of Reclamation.

Let us look first at the policy limiting the size of farm. This 160-acre limitation is a maximum. Limits as low as 40 acres have been used. In at least one such instance, the project was not an intensive agriculture, and the 40-acre limit was a serious mistake. With the expansion of the reclamation program during the thirties, the policy of making homes on the land for the largest possible number of people gained favor. We see a culmination of this in the settlement plans for the Columbia Basin Project. Here the farm size was based on a minimum acceptable income and varied on lands of different productivity to attain some uniformity in farm income. Thus, say some observers, the reclamation program is in danger of being oversold as a Western population measure rather than for the development of an efficient commercial agriculture. These same observers argue for efficient commercial family farms rather than something approaching subsistence farming, as did the first plans for the Columbia Basin Project.

It does not seem that the 160-acre limit unduly restricts the farm size on private lands within reclamation projects, since husband and wife may have 160 acres each. On two reclamation projects ,however—one in Colorado and one in Nevada—the 160-acre limit was removed by special Congressional enactment.

Similar legislation is now sought for the California Central Valley Project, where some rather large land holdings would be affected by the limitation. It is argued, perhaps with some reason, that in some locations in the San Joaquin Valley the 160-acre limitation could not be made effective because of the importance of irrigation from wells. This argument contends that some farms using well irrigation could avoid the effect of the acreage limitation by staying out of the project, yet benefiting from any recharge of underground water reserves resulting from the project.

When the Reclamation Act of 1902 provided for the use of interest-free money to develop the Western reclamation projects, the justification for that policy was that the money received into the federal treasury from the public lands of the West would be set aside as a reclamation fund—a revolving fund into which repayments would be made and from which new projects would be financed. This fund is now nonliquid because of the magnitude of the program and the slow turnover of the investment. However, on that part of the cost of reclamation projects charged to power development, interest is now paid from the power revenues. This is paid into the federal treasury, not into the reclamation fund.

Repayment contracts on the reclamation projects may be for forty years, and another ten years may be used in the organization and development phases of a project. A maximum of fifty years is allowable for repayment, consequently, without any interest charge on the investment. This rather long repayment period and the absence of an interest charge have been important factors in slow repayments for many of these projects. A study shows that, as of 1938, the repayment rates were such that only half of the federal-reclamation farm obligations to the project would pay out in seventy-five years. The other half would take longer. However, a recent analysis by the Bureau of Reclamation shows that in 1946 the repayments on these projects were very nearly current. The delinquency was shown to be $1,800,-000 on irrigation contracts totaling $352,000,000. Authorized charge-offs total some $17,000,000.

It does seem that from now on the cause of Western reclamation would be well served by the inclusion of a moderate interest rate for funds from the federal treasury. It also seems desirable, as an incentive for earlier repayments on the farm contracts, that provision be made for clear title to the buyer as soon as the obligation on the farm is fully paid. Under present law and policy, this is not possible because the joint-liability clause makes clear title possible only after all obligations by all buyers have been met. There have been instances where this joint-liability requirement has been set aside by Congressional action.

A recent policy developed by the Bureau of Reclamation, under the Reclamation Act of 1939, would, in effect, vest the title to the water supplies of a project in the federal government and provide the water to the users on long-term rental contracts. That is, the water would be handled on a public-utility basis. The argument for this is that it lowers the cost to the user, since he is not paying for amortization, and gives both buyer and seller some latitude in use of the water supply. There has been some rather violent objection to this policy because it places too much power with the government bureau. It should be possible to define this power satisfactorily and to make use of the principle involved, which has a good economic basis for some situations. There are situations where supplemental irrigation is quite valuable in some years and is little needed in others, as a result of crop rotations and annual differences in rainfall and temperatures. This policy should not be ruled out so that it cannot be applied to these situations.

Under present policy, power revenues from reclamation projects are scheduled to repay a larger share of the irrigation cost of the projects than is the irrigated agriculture. This is to say that urban economy is being taxed, in some degree, to subsidize the rural economy. Results from this policy seem obscure. Some observers state that the agriculture might benefit more from lower power rates and a consequent greater industrial stimulus, even though the direct subsidy to the project might be less.

161

Under provisions of the Reclamation Act of 1939, the Bureau of Reclamation was given the right, after investigation of a possible project, to express its approval or authorization of a project if the results of the investigation were favorable. But the development of the project must await Congressional authorization and appropriation of funds. This policy has been challenged, especially by the residents of California. Their thought is that there should be no prior or preliminary "choice" between projects by the Bureau of Reclamation, as a guide to political action in Congress. But in this matter there is some disposition on the part of other Western states to look askance at California, with her large and growing political strength. In June, 1948, Congress repealed this provision of the Reclamation Act of 1939.

These several features of social policy that are evolving in reclamation law and in the administration of that law can mean much to the future development of the West. The policies should be analyzed for their time and place of application, and their results, where possible, should be measured and studied.

What About Private Reclamation?

Private business enterprise has developed most of the present irrigation of the West. All of the five million acres of California and most of the three and one-quarter million acres of Colorado have been developed as private business. Nearly 90 per cent of the present total acreage has been developed by private enterprise, without the benefit of interest-free money, without any charge-off of construction costs against flood control or other public values, and usually without any subsidy from hydroelectric power revenues.

We cannot conclude, however, that the present eighteen million acres of irrigation developed by private business enterprise has been an unqualified business success, or that these enterprises have had no subsidy. Bondholders and other investors— including farmers who lost their farms—have contributed some large "subsidies" to many of these private irrigation developments through losses in the financial reorganization of the businesses. Speculative promotion and overcapitalization have caused financial problems for irrigation developments that, since financial reorganization, have proved sound. Recently the vice-president in charge of loans for a large life insurance company referred to an extensive and now successful privately developed irrigated area as "having a horrible financial record."

Expansion of irrigated areas beyond their water supply, inclusion of unproductive land, and other defects of planning are additional causes of reorganization and financial losses in private irrigation developments. But despite the financial losses in reorganization, most of the private-enterprise irrigation developments of the West are now going concerns.

Present expansion of Western irrigation is coming mainly from federal reclamation projects. Projects now under construction or authorized for construction cover a total of some ten million acres. Additional projects now under investigation for federal development contains several million acres of possible irrigable land. How much of this planned federal reclamation might be undertaken as private-enterprise development, and what public measures might make possible more of that type of development?

Most of the private-enterprise irrigation projects, whether organized as co-operatives, partnerships, or corporations, have been of comparatively small size. They have not had ready access to capital markets, and they have lacked engineering and agricultural technical aid in planning and construction. Much of the private-enterprise irrigation of the West has depended upon direct diversion of the stream flow or upon such diversion with inadequate supplemental water storages. Lack of late-season water has been the usual result, especially for the low-priority water rights. This disadvantage of private-enterprise irrigation development has resulted in a federal reclamation development to provide supplemental water to privately developed irrigation.

163

Such federal reclamation now serves about two million acres of private irrigation, in addition to the two million acres of federal reclamation development. Almost half of the ten million acres in authorized federal reclamation development is for supplemental water to privately developed irrigated areas.

If private enterprise is to have a part in the future expansion of Western irrigation, it must be through enterprises of considerable size. Irrigation which can be accomplished by direct stream diversion and small supplemental storages has now been fully done, perhaps overdone. Public measures and aids to facilitate organization on an adequate scale, to give easier access to capital markets, and to help in engineering planning and in land-use planning would give the most needed help to private irrigation development.

But we should remember that the large water storages involved in the recent and in the planned federal reclamation projects usually have important public-interest values—such as flood control, sanitation, navigation, and recreation—and that these storages have several purposes, not just irrigation development. Permanent federal government management of the reservoirs is intended for these developments.

VII. Transition in Forestry

Experts who have studied the timber resources, the forest-growth capacity, and the timber uses of the United States tell us that the drain on our saw-timber resources now exceeds, and for many years past has exceeded, growth rates by one-third to one-half.

But, they tell us, we have the capacity to grow adequate timber, just by using our present forest lands well. They also tell us that unless we begin doing just that, now, the timber scarcity will be acute in another twenty to forty years.

Forest-resource studies give us the general outline of where and what this resource is, nationally. We need this picture as the guide for national forestry policy and program development. Approximately one-third of our present saw-timber reserves are on public lands, mostly the Western public lands. But the capacity to grow timber rests largely with the privately held forest lands. Some estimates place this private forest-land growth capacity at 90 per cent of the total, the public-land capacity at 10 per cent. Timber growth rates are slow on many of the Western public lands. We have timber reserves on these lands because of our public-land timber conservation policy.

A forestry program for growing a timber crop must look primarily to the privately owned forest lands. The forest-resource timber survey conducted for some years by the Forest Service in the Department of Agriculture shows that this privately owned forest land may logically be classed into four main types of ownership: (1) large forest ownerships, (2) medium-sized forest ownerships, (3) small forest ownerships, and (4) farm wood lots. In this survey, forest ownerships greater than 50,000 acres are classed as large, between 50,000 and 5,000 acres as medium, and under 5,000 as small. The farm wood lots, timber lands within farms, average 43 acres in size.

Large forest ownerships account for about 14 per cent of total private forest-land ownership, medium-sized ownerships for 10 per cent, small ownerships for 36 per cent, and the farm wood lots for approximately 40 per cent. There are some four hundred of the large forest ownerships, thirty-two hundred of the medium-sized forest ownerships, approximately one million of the small forest holdings, and nearly three and one-quarter million of the farm wood lot ownerships.

With this picture of forest-land productive capacity and ownership before us and with timber scarcity and higher prices now foreseeable, we may ask why the individual initiative and planning of private forestry will not give us all of the results that can be had. Why do we need any national forestry policy and program other than that of extension forestry work and of furnishing the forest-land owners with information about the future market supply, demand, and price outlook?

Some of the influences that form the "economic climate" for private forestry give us the answer to this question.

We have always had, and still have, sufficient natural timber reserves to cause the market price of timber to be a "supply price," and essentially a cost-of-harvesting price rather than a cost-of-production-and-cost-of-harvesting price. There is nothing quite comparable to this in the price economics of our agricultural crops. But we now can see the end of this price situation. We can foresee that before long a scarcity of timber may cause prices to be determined on the demand side of our price economics, perhaps considerably above production and marketing costs. But we do not know just how soon this will be, and a future, uncertain price does not motivate many private forest-land owners to increase their expenditures to make fuller use of their forest-land capacity. Price motivation will not come, for most forest-land owners, until forest reserves are nearly gone.

166

Price motivation for full use of our forest-land capacity is, then, still in the future. Only a relative few of the forest-land owners can foresee that turn in price, and yet fewer are in a position to finance the waiting period necessary for an appreciable increase in forest production. Especially is this true of the small forest-land owners and the farm wood-lot owners. Forest-land ownerships of these two classes are, in general, rather poorly managed and used.

If we are to avoid the eventual reality of that much-heralded timber famine, we cannot await the price motivation of private forestry. What are the alternatives? We do now have some aids to private forestry. We have forestry extension work through the land-grant colleges and, with this, distribution of planting stock from government-owned tree nurseries. We have co-operative federal-state-private fire protection. We have provision for federal-state organization of forest-management units to aid in the preparation and execution of management plans on private forest lands. All of these measures are valuable and are accomplishing good results. None of these measures is financed to the extent necessary to do a full-scale job.

The need for a national program for forest production has now reached such a point that nothing but a strenuous program appears able to do the job. The program which we propose here is strenuous. It calls for continuous use, during the next several decades, of something comparable to the "Production Goals" program that was used effectively through the recent war period by the Department of Agriculture to attain the needed production of certain critical crops.

In the organization for this work, the Department of Agriculture made the national analysis of crop-supply requirements and production capacities. A tentative analysis, by states, of crop-acreage capacities and production goals was then sent to state boards for further analysis and corrections. Finally the goal figures, showing county acreages, acreage shifts, and desirable changes in management practices, went to a county board. At the county level, the goals were analyzed into community or area figures and then into individual farm goals. This is, of course, an oversimplification of the procedure. A totaling of the individual farm data caused some recasting of county and state goals, and there was no attempt to "enforce" individual farm crop-acreage goals. Most important in the program was the two-way road between the farms and the Department of Agriculture. The farm operator knew the direction and intention of the goal effort and had as his guides the incentives of price supports, or "forward pricing," and direct benefit payments for certain accomplishments.

A similar organization and procedure could be set up to stimulate and guide our national forestry production. We now have a sufficient national inventory of timber stands and timber capacity to make the first effort at the national level on national and state goals. In the next step—carrying the tentative state goals down to the counties and the individuals—we would soon learn more about the current forest situation and potential capacity of the country than we could ever learn through surveys.

This program cannot provide a smooth and easy road. Some knotty problems of forest management, forest economics, and resource policy would have to be resolved in working out the pricing and other incentives—regionally and locally—for forest planting, stand improvement, and other important phases of forest management. This program would necessarily include a provision for forward pricing of timber. It would mean incentive payments to individuals, to attain certain management objectives. Perhaps forest insurance and forest credits would have to be available as a part of this program.

But the organization and execution of such a program does not seem to present any insuperable difficulties. Perhaps it is just about the only way to get the job done.

PUBLIC AIDS TO PRIVATE FORESTRY

MUCH OF OUR FUTURE TIMBER CROP must come from some one million small forest ownerships and about three and one-quarter million farm wood-lot enterprises. These small forest and farm woodland owners usually lack technical knowledge of forest and woodland management. In recognition of these facts, several co-operative federal-state-local programs have been developed to aid private forestry. These programs include the furnishing of planting stock to private owners, the extension of information on forest and wood-lot management, aid in fire suppression, and on-the-ground technical aid in forest management.

Under the provisions of the Clark-McNary and Norris-Doxey acts, tree nursery stock is grown in nurseries owned and operated by the states, with federal aid, and this stock is distributed at somewhat less than cost to small forest owners and to farm woodland owners. Some forty-three million acres of farm woodlands need planting to make them productive. Some of this will seed naturally during the course of the next twenty-five years, but more than half of this acreage will not restock unless it is planted. In the past twenty years, only one million acres have been planted; the total job would require about four hundred years at this rate. More educational and technical aid is needed for these forest and woodland owners, but the greatest need is a greater output of nursery stock. Present nursery output is less than half the demand, and this demand could be and should be greatly expanded. The present yearly output of fifty million trees should be increased twentyfold.

Co-operative federal-state forestry extension work is now operative in forty-six states. Primarily the objective of this work is to develop interest in improved forest and woodland management and to teach landowners how to grow timber crops and how to get better use of the forest products on the farm. This extension work is understaffed and inadequate; the present force of sixty-five extension foresters would need to be increased at least threefold to provide an adequate staff for this work. In some states where interest in farm forestry has lagged, the extension forestry work has turned to the horticultural field rather than to farm woodland management.

Aid to private forestry in fire suppression is organized under the provisions of the Clark-McNary Act of 1924. Where fire danger is serious on private forest lands, fire suppression districts are organized, and the owners contribute part of the cost and are a part of the suppression organization. Approximately seventeen million dollars was spent on this co-operative federal-state-local fire suppression work in 1946. Federal funds paid 42 per cent of this, state and county funds 44 per cent, and forest owners' funds 14 per cent. Federal government participation in this program has been limited to nine million dollars annually. To date, this assistance has been made available to only one-fourth of the small forest and woodland owners. It is estimated that to do a full-sized job would cost about thirty-two million dollars annually.

A great deal of technical aid is given farm-forest owners by extension foresters. This provision of the Clark-McNary Act was amplified and specialized somewhat by the Norris-Doxey Act. This latter act provides for the organization, by counties or by groups of counties, of co-operative farm-woodland management projects. These projects then become the vehicle for technical service in forest management to the owners by federal and state foresters. In 1946, there were 156 of these projects operating in some 600 counties in 39 states. Where the states contribute 50 per cent or more of the cost of these projects, the co-operating state agency—the state agricultural extension service or the state forestry department—has direct supervision of the project. Otherwise, the United States Forest Service has the supervision of the project.

This co-operative management program, which is just getting underway, can become the most valuable of all the present aids to private forestry, for the work must be local, adapted, and on-the-ground. A great variety of farm-forest management conditions and problems present themselves, and general principles and instruction are of little practical value unless accompanied by a technician's analysis of conditions and needs of individual properties. Such service as this means technical aid primarily and educational work secondarily. In nearly all of the states where this work is now operative, it is handled by the state forester, who, in some instances, is authorized to charge a fee when much work is involved. The demand for this kind of technical help is so great that only about one-tenth of all applicants can be served by the approximately two hundred foresters available.

Thus we see that the programs that have been developed to aid private forestry have yet to expand to full scope, and we may need some recasting of emphasis among these programs. Especially desirable may be a clearer delineation of the organization and interrelationship of the forestry extension program and the Norris-Doxey program to give technical aid and service to groups of forest and woodland owners.

FEDERAL FORESTRY PROGRAMS

THERE ARE TWO MAIN TYPES of federal forestry programs. One of these is the management of public land for forest production and conservation. The other concerns public policy in the use and management of private land for forest production.

Management of the national forests for forest production constitutes the principal, though not the only, federal public-land program for forest management. Our national-forest system now includes land in forty states and in Alaska, and the net area of national-forest land now totals about 180,000,000 acres. Gross area within the boundary of the national forests now totals some 228,000,000 acres. This means that within the boundaries of the national forests are some 48,000,000 acres of private, state, and other ownerships.

171

Most of the Western national forests were reserved from the public domain, but those east of the hundredth meridian have been developed mainly through acquisition of private land. Acquisition of private land has also substantially increased the acreage of some of the Western national forests. These lands are purchased with funds appropriated by Congress, or acquired through the exchange of timber on the national forests for private lands, usually cutover forest lands.

Timber stands on the national forests are protected from fire and insects, insofar as feasible, and are managed for a sustained yield. Reforestation is undertaken on cutover or burned-over lands that are acquired and on the national forest burns, which sometimes cover large acreages. Within the national forests of the United States is nearly one-third of our total remaining reserves of saw timber, but these lands are not yet furnishing any large part of our present cut. It seems best to maintain these reserves in the national forests and even to add to them. They are going to be needed as a cushion in the transition, which must be made over the next forty years, to the sustained-yield management of privately owned forest lands.

Comparatively recent in the timber management program for the national forests is the organization of co-operative sustained-yield units. Under federal legislation enacted in 1944 (Public Law 273, of March 29), private, state or other forest land within or near national forests may, through co-operative agreements, be organized with national-forest land into sustained-yield units. All of the lands are then operated under a management program designed to give a permanent annual timber harvest and to assure good management and high production for the forest lands and timber stands.

Other federal public lands—besides the national forests—on which timber stands and timber management are of some importance are the national parks, the "O and C" lands, and the public-domain lands. A branch of forestry was organized in the National Park Service, in 1933, to manage the forest resources

172

Cut out and get out

Selective cutting for sustained yield

of the national parks and to protect those resources from fire. Approximately half of the total area of the national parks requires fire protection. Timber is regarded as a part of the scenic and recreational values of the national parks and is not harvested commercially.

Management of the O and C lands presents a unique problem in federal forestry. These lands, some two and a half million acres in extent, were recovered by the federal government from the former Oregon and California and Coos Bay Wagon Road grants. These lands, which are located in western Oregon, lie in a checkerboard pattern of alternate sections, intermingled with national forest and privately owned land. This is a rich timber resource, with reserves aggregating some fifty billion board feet. This land now has fire protection, and there is authority for the pooling of interests of the owners of intermingled lands and the formation of sustained-yield management units. Primary responsibility for the management of the O and C lands rests with a forestry unit of the Bureau of Land Management in the Department of the Interior.

It is estimated that some twenty million acres of forest land remain in the public domain. Some of this is high mountain land, but probably most of it is in the juniper or piñon-juniper zone or the oak brush zone. This land now has but limited forest management, yet we may, in time, find values for these forest resources that are not now appreciated.

Federal forestry programs in the realm of public policy for private forestry are, mainly, those that extend direct aid to private forestry and those that develop scientific information for private forestry. Through its branch of State and Private Forestry, the Forest Service provides national leadership in the administration of the Clark-McNary and the Norris-Doxey acts for aid to private forestry. Through its branch of Research, the Forest Service conducts scientific study in forest management, the results of which are made available to private forestry through publications and through federal-state extension work.

173

In its Forest Products Laboratory at Madison, Wisconsin, the Forest Service has developed important new principles in wood technology and wood use. This work—which includes experiments with bonded lamination and compression and chemical impregnation of woods and wood cellulose—has greatly extended the use of the secondary tree species and the substitution of these for the more costly and scarcer woods. The scope of the work of this laboratory appears to be developing remarkably.

We need this second type of federal forestry program to give leadership to the national and state programs aiding private forestry, to develop over-all forestry policy, and to do scientific work in forestry. Probably these aspects of federal forestry programs are neither so generally nor so well known as is the public forest-land management, but they are of great importance to the future of our national forestry production. Management of the national forests has important national objectives beyond forest production.

State Forests and State Forestry

A REALISTIC VIEW of our future forest production and forest-land use must take into account the large acreages of forest land now privately owned that should go into public ownership. This is true because our forest economics do not afford the business incentive for forest production on much of the cutover, burned-over, and low-yield forest land. But there is a public interest in this land, not only to have such land contribute to a vital future timber crop, but to conserve the forest-land resource.

Much of this land should go into state forests and could do so without any conflict with the future development of the national forests. It should, in fact, be possible to define the policies that would guide national forestry and state forestry in their future selection for acquisition of lands for public forestry. Such a definition of policy, by helping to avoid conflicts, should give an impetus to both federal and state forestry and to federal and

174

state co-operation in the development and management of public forests.

In the evolving of a set of policies concerning the future-development spheres of state and national forests, certain basic policies seem fairly clear at the outset. Lands to be acquired for a system of national forests should be those with a high long-range public interest, regional or national in scope. Usually the objective would be watershed protection, long-time investment in forest production, or the retirement and restoration of submarginal land. Lands to be acquired for state forests should be those with important local values for wood supply, wildlife propagation and recreation. This does not mean that there would be no state forests with a primary objective of long-range forest production, but such state forests probably would be limited in area and scope.

New York, Pennsylvania, and Minnesota have led the way in the development of state forests. Thirty-eight states have adopted a policy of establishing and maintaining forest reservations. It is estimated that there now is a total of about fifteen million acres of forest land in state ownership, though only a part of this is organized in forest reservations, and some of it is not under any forest management other than protection from fire. Of special importance in the future of state forest development is the need to provide support for an efficient administration for management of the state forests.

It is estimated in the Copeland Report of 1933[1] that the public ownership of forest lands should, eventually, be increased by a total of 224,000,000 acres. The report of the chief of the Forest Service for the year 1938 estimated that 148,314,000 acres of forest land now in private ownership should, in time, be acquired by public agencies. This estimate indicated that probably some 48,000,000 acres of this total might be best suited for state and community forests and that approximately 100,000,000 acres would be best acquired as national-forest land. Some 40,000,000

[1] *A National Plan for American Forestry*, 73 Cong., Sen. Doc. 12.

acres of this 100,000,000 acres are within the boundaries of existing national forests.

If the past is a reliable guide, progress in the acquirement of forest lands for federal and state forests will be slow—too slow. There is not as yet much public awareness of this program or of its needs. As a consequence, use of only limited funds for public acquisition of forest land is taken for granted. Some local opposition to acquisition of land for national forests has developed, and in some cases this might have been avoided by a better definition of policy for federal and state forest-land acquisition.

State forests in programs for state forestry are largely in the future, though they may become quite important. Most of the work of state forestry now consists in the administration of state forestry laws by a forestry department or division in the executive branch of the state government. These laws concern the use and control of fire on forest lands; the regulation of cutting and of other management practices to keep forest land productive (fifteen states now have such regulatory legislation); the taxation of forest lands in such a manner as to encourage good forest management; fencing to control domestic livestock against damage to forest growth; and a number of other measures designed to aid forestry.

Although there is a considerable body of state law designed to aid forestry, much of it appears to be inoperative or ineffective. Especially does this appear to be true of the laws to regulate cutting and other aspects of forest management. Legislation for forestry taxation does not affect a significant acreage of forest land. There are special forest-tax laws in twenty-six states— mostly optional exemption and yield-tax legislation providing for exclusion of immature timber from the property-tax base or for substitution of a severance tax. In more than half of these twenty-six states, less than 1 per cent of the private commercial forest land has been classified under such laws, and in none of the twenty-six states is more than 8 per cent of such land so classified.

State forests and state forestry can be and must be an important part of public forestry. Much of our necessary future regulation of forest-land use and of forest-management practices must come through state law and state administration. Technical aid and service to organized groups of forest owners—a federal-state program now getting under way—depends upon effective state forestry administration. Other established services, such as fire suppression, can expand to the needed coverage only through an expansion and development of state forestry.

What Is Wrong with Farm Forestry?

On some three and one-fourth million farms of the United States—one out of every two—farm forestry is an enterprise of some importance. This farm enterprise varies, regionally and locally, from relatively unimportant to highly important in the economy of the farms. Fewer corn-belt farms have woodland enterprises, and those enterprises are usually of small relative importance in the farm income. In parts of the New England states, the Lake states, and the South, farm-forest enterprises are more numerous and are more important in the farm economy. Often the farm-forest enterprise becomes a major enterprise for farms in these regions.

In the aggregate, farm forestry constitutes a very important part of our total national resource in forest land and forest crop. It is estimated that farm woodlands contain approximately one-third of our total national capacity for forest production. We must look to farm forestry for a third of our needed future timber production, and the farm woodlands must be well managed to contribute their share of our future timber needs.

But these farm woodlands are not generally well managed and productive. They are the most poorly managed of all the different types of forest-land ownerships and forest enterprises. More often than not, the farm woodlands are "high-graded," or clear-cut; they are understocked in both quantity and quality; they are overgrazed, grazed unseasonally, or grazed with the

177

wrong kind of livestock; and they are ravaged with fire, both intentionally and accidentally.

The one most important factor in this situation is the lack of a good system of farm-forestry credits and the absence of the inspection and management aid—such as now accompanies livestock credit or any other specialized agricultural credit—that would accompany farm-forestry credit. This credit feature is important because a forest enterprise requires long-term, low-rate investment. Most farmers are not that kind of investors. A good system of farm-forest credit would remove the one problem which the farmer is in no position to meet: the present depletion of farm woodland growing-stand capital.

Concerning the depletion of farm woodland growing-stand capital and the importance of farm-forest credit, an experienced forester has this to say:

"In order to have anything approaching maximum productivity on woodland, we need from 3,000 to 6,000 board feet of growing stock per acre. Here in the Arkansas Ozarks we actually have an average growing stock of 500 board feet per acre. Even in those areas where the annual growth increment is excellent—say 6 per cent of the growing stock—6 per cent of 500 board feet per acre amounts to nearly nothing. Yet an average growth increment of 3 per cent on a growing stand of 5,000 board feet gives a reasonably good return per acre.

"It seems that our present timber economics are, however, such as to foster a reduction of our growing stock to a minimum, and to hold a very large percentage of our woodland at near-zero productivity. If a farm operator is to keep an average of 5,000 board feet of growing stock per acre on his farm woodland, he will have invested in the needed growing stand approximately fifty dollars an acre. He must carry this investment, with average management, for an annual return of 2 to 3 per cent. If he is to establish a growing stock on depleted lands, his waiting period will be longer and his return lower. If we are to have successful farm forestry, some way must be found to provide cheaper credit than that now available to the individual farmer. Under present conditions, the investment in the farm woodland is ever at the mercy of the financial emergencies which can, at any time, beset the small owner.

"Here is a good illustration of the point I wish to make. A well-to-do farmer had co-operated for fifteen years or more with the state extension forester in the management of the woodland of his farm. This farmer had cut his woodlot selectively and had brought it to a good state of productivity. Suddenly he had the misfortune of a serious injury, and could not continue the operation of his farm. He and his family decided that they must sell the farm and that they must sell the timber first, since that was the only way to get the real value out of it. The timber was sold and the stands were clear-cut—an end result not different from that to be expected from an ill-informed and hard-up farmer and a greedy timber buyer.

"It seems certain that in this instance where the farmer decided he must sell the timber before sale of the farm in order to realize the value of the timber, a most important influence was the fact that the federal land banks and other land-credit agencies and institutions have in the past been reluctant to base any part of a land loan on a growing stand of timber. This is not a criticism of the policy of the banks. Their experience has showed them that when a loan was so based the timber too often "walked," and when it became necessary to foreclose a mortgage, the timber was invariably gone.

"Surely it should be possible to meet this problem of farm-forestry credit in a system of specialized forest credits, with adequate provision for inspection."

This plea of a forester for a well-adapted system of forest credits has a good basis of reality in forest economics and in farm-forest management. Such a system of credits would not solve all of the problems of farm forestry, but it would no doubt result in significant gains for this important segment of our total forest economy.

179

VIII. Flood-Control and Drainage Programs and Policies

GOOD AND BAD FLOOD CONTROL

ONE WAY TO SOLVE the flood-control and drainage problems of a river basin is to flood permanently much of the land that suffers from floods—the valley lands—by a system of reservoirs. The pattern of land use and farm types must then make the adjustments occasioned by the loss of the valley lands. The other approach to flood control rests upon maximum reliance on land-use measures to infiltrate the water where it falls, with a minimum dependence on reservoirs along the stream valleys. We now seem to favor the former of these two policies, stated as extremes above, in our national program of flood control.

This is not a forestudied and planned policy. Events have forced it upon us. A change in the present circumstances sufficient to permit an extensive change in our flood-control policy will take some time. The chain of events that have led to our present policy started in the headwaters lands of the stream basins. Too much arable agriculture, too little forest cover, inadequate pasture and cover crops for farmed lands, and drainage reclamation of natural wet lands—all of these influences cause a flood-control and drainage problem for the valley bottom lands of the headwater areas of major stream basins. To counteract these influences, drainage works are constructed on such bottom lands, levees are built along the streams, channels are dredged and straightened, and the water is speeded downstream. The cumulative effect is floods—higher and higher floods—in the lower reaches of a river basin, and a demand by landowners and cities downstream for flood-control reservoirs upstream.

We are now building, in some localities in the Mississippi basin, upstream flood-control reservoirs as a result of just such

180

a chain of events. In the construction of the reservoirs, we lose the production of the valley bottom lands and so lose the complementary feed-production relationship of rich river-bottom farm lands to the prairie pasture lands. The consequence is likely to be more arable agriculture on hill lands that should be in pasture, more soil loss, poorer water conservation, more rapid sedimentation of the flood-control reservoirs, and impoverishment of the lands and of the rural life of the area.

This is the chain of events that can result from ruinous land use in the headwater areas of a river basin. After the first of these events reaches a certain stage, it seems very difficult to avoid the consequent events. Change in the use of land in the headwater areas—the method of correction alternative to the construction of flood-control reservoirs—then seems too slow in its corrective effects. Can we at least lessen the need for reservoirs by changed land use, where we have reached the multiple-reservoir stage in a flood control problem? Can we forestall the reservoir stage, which now seems near in many situations, by a sufficiently vigorous land-use approach to an incipient flood-control problem?

Any approach to flood control through change in land use in the headwater areas will have to be a vigorous program. It is a most important approach and the one that must finally gain ascendancy over reservoir-building. If the land-use method of river-basin flood control is to become effective, it must be carried out through a conservation division or agency of the Department of Agriculture. Such agency must have the power to correlate all other public conservation programs in its zone of operation.

Included in the headwater land-use approach to flood control must be a rather wide scope of alternatives, ranging from land acquisition for restoration of reclaimed upstream wet lands, or natural "sponge" areas, and for afforestation of severely eroded farm lands, to the influencing of farm practices and land use by co-operative management, subsidy payments, or regulation.

The timely use of this approach can, in many situations, avoid

181

the arrival of a flood-control problem at the stage where costly reservoirs are necessary. Can we develop this kind of program, or must we wait for the acute flood problems to motivate us, and then bring in the upstream land use only as a weak supplement to a program of building reservoirs, levees, river channels, drainage works, river-diversion flood areas, and other means to handle an excessive volume of water in the streams?

RIVER ENGINEERING AND LAND USE IN
FLOOD CONTROL

DURING THE FISCAL YEAR 1948, some four hundred million dollars was appropriated by Congress for expenditure by the Army Corps of Engineers on flood controls. During this same period, as a part of the federal government flood-control program, about four million dollars was allotted for expenditures by the Department of Agriculture, to be used to improve land use and soil and water conservation on the watersheds. We may soon decide that there expenditures are very much out of proportion to their relative importance.

River engineering is essential to flood control. Even under pristine conditions in their watersheds, the streams of the humid parts of the United States sometimes rampaged over lands that are now settled and developed. But under those pristine conditions, the capacity of the lands to absorb and retain the precipitation of heavy storms was far greater than now. We cannot restore the original conditions in the watersheds, but we can reverse the present progressive deterioration in the ability of these lands to absorb and retain water.

Changes in the use of lands can reduce, by as much as one-half, the peak runoff from storms of moderate intensity. For storms of longer duration and higher intensity, good condition and use of the watershed lands may not reduce the peak runoff by more than one-fourth, compared with poor watershed conditions. These figures are guesses, based upon the limited avail-

182

able information from observations and experiments. Forested land with a deep litter and forest soil has a high capacity for water infiltration and retention. This may also be said of cropped land with deep topsoil and a good vegetative cover. The contrast between such land and lands with thin and eroded topsoil is said to be enormous. We do not yet know what we can do, and may have to do, in watershed land use for flood control. Yet we do know that the present trend in the use and the conditions of the major-stream watershed lands is sending those streams to new high in flood crests. This is an accelerating trend.

Meanwhile we spend billions on river engineering for flood control—on dams, levees, dredging, dikes, channel straightening, and other engineering devices—to control the water in the rivers rather than keep more of it in the watershed for a longer time. Probably for some time we shall need to increase our efforts on river engineering for flood control, for land-use measures develop slowly and do not bear fruit quickly. Land use for flood control must now be a long-time program, and we may be able to get at it only as a part of an agricultural conservation program rather than as a full-scale land-use phase of a flood-control program. Perhaps the federal government flood-control studies and evaluation of the benefits of flood control could afford some measure of the public expenditures for flood control that should be directed through the agricultural conservation programs of the Department of Agriculture. Most of the known measures for flood control through improved land use could be embodied in those programs.

The four million dollars referred to above, for expenditure on the land-use features of flood control, is assigned to Department of Agriculture conservation agencies such as the Soil Conservation Service and the Forest Service. These funds are used for such purposes as terracing farm land, contour cultivation, strip cropping, pasture furrowing, gully stabilizing, changes in use of land from crops to pasture or forestry, and small dams.

Although it may not come soon enough, the land-use phase

of flood control will likely become an important and full-scale effort, in what we may hope will be an effective organizational setting.

WESTERN FLOODS ARE DIFFERENT

SOMETIMES THIS QUESTION IS RAISED: Why flood control in the arid West, where the lands below 7,000 feet elevation seldom yield much runoff and the stream channels have a high gradient? A good question! It is true that we seldom see, west of the hundredth meridian, settled agricultural lands inundated by heavy and extensive precipitation.

Floods in the humid parts of the United States have been much influenced by the use of land, but there would be some destructive floods even with ideal uses of land and with the best possible hydrologic conditions in the watershed. There are few comparable flood conditions in the West—that is, floods resulting from the lands of a large drainage area becoming fully saturated and the consequent flow of the precipitation into the stream channels. But there are Western floods—destructive and sometimes locally disastrous floods.

Most of the destructive Western floods result from a combination of three conditions: the frequently torrential nature of summer storms in an arid country; precipitous upland watersheds above a settled agricultural valley or plain; denudation of range and forest cover from an upland watershed area. These conditions have produced floods and disaster repeatedly along the Rocky Mountains, in the Intermountain valleys, in Southern California, in the California Central Valley, and elsewhere. These floods are localized, compared with those of the Mississippi Valley, but they are intense and severely destructive in the locality where they strike. An awesome, grinding mass of water, boulders, mud, and debris surges down a steep mountain-stream course and obliterates farm lands and homes below.

In most cases, these floods would not have occurred had the

upland watershed lands been in good condition. Intense but brief and local rainfall on denuded areas, high upon the slopes and ridges, loosens the thunderous masses of soil and rock that go roaring down a mountain canyon. These denuded areas may be only a minor percentage of the basin that is the flood source, yet the flood would not occur but for the denuded areas. A good cover would infiltrate enough of the precipitation to give adequate protection to the soils on the mountain slopes so that nothing more than a freshet of roily water would appear below. This statement has been challenged, but as evidence of its truth is the fact that the floods along the Wasatch front in Utah have buried under debris the soils that have remained undisturbed since they were formed as deltas under the prehistoric Lake Bonneville.

These floods have occurred, in about the same manner, in widely separated Western localities. They have swept into the environs of Los Angeles because fires have denuded the brush and ground litter from the San Gabriel and the San Bernadino uplands. They have plagued the Utah towns between Provo and Brigham because of the overgrazed bald spots high above on the slopes and ridges of the Wasatch. They have roared through Pueblo, Colorado, because of overgrazing and erosion along the steep slopes of the canyon of the Arkansas River. We shall likely have many more of these floods before we become convinced of the need for corrective action and undertake sufficiently vigorous corrective measures.

It is evident that Western flood-control work must come primarily through land-use measures. There are some localities where deterioration of a mountain watershed area is so critical that, at the outset, engineering work must complement the changed use of the land. One such locality is the uplands that were the source of the flood that nearly destroyed Centerville, Utah. Here, large contour trenches were constructed on the critical upland areas, the areas were reseeded, and the watershed was closed to grazing. However, most of the Western flood control is primarily a matter of good land management in the uplands—

good range management, good forestry, and conservation of the upland soils.

On the Sacramento and Columbia rivers, there are some problems of flood control comparable with those of the humid part of the United States. In fact, for six months of the year parts of the drainage areas of these streams are humid. It cannot be said, consequently, that flood-control work for these rivers must rest entirely on land use. Neither should it be inferred that land use in the uplands of the Sacramento and of the Columbia is not highly important in the work of flood control for these drainages.

FIFTY MILLION NEW ACRES

IT IS CONSERVATIVELY ESTIMATED that the drainage of wet lands has added more than one hundred million acres of cultivated land to the total cultivated area of the United States. This is almost one-fourth of our present cropland acreage.

All of this drainage reclamation of agricultural land has been undertaken as private enterprise. We have no counterpart, in drainage reclamation, of the work of the Federal Bureau of Reclamation. Federal irrigation reclamation accounts for only two million acres out of the approximately twenty million acres of Western irrigation development. However, the Federal Bureau of Reclamation now has some ten million acres of proposed irrigation projects authorized for construction. Most of this acreage is, of necessity, privately-owned land. There remains only limited opportunity for irrigation reclamation of the Western public-domain lands.

Is there a substantial remaining acreage of wet lands reclaimable through drainage for agricultural use? Do we need such reclamation? Where and what are the remaining wet lands that might be reclaimed through drainage? What are the comparisons of costs and production for irrigation reclamation of Western arid lands and for drainage reclamation of Eastern wet lands?

Recent compilations of the available information by the Department of Agriculture shows something of the possibility for augmenting our present cropland acreage through drainage reclamation. These compilations show a total of nearly fifty million acres of drainable wet lands that are undeveloped for agricultural use or that are partially developed and partially farmed. Some of these lands lie within organized drainage enterprises, some outside. The drainage data referred to were compiled to show acreages of drainable wet lands within and outside of such organized drainage enterprises.

The first compilation, titled "Acreage of Land in Organized Drainage Enterprises, the Drainage Improvements of Which Can Be Rehabilitated at Reasonable Cost," shows a total acreage of 28,928,000. Some 24,700,000 acres of these lands are cultivated or partly cultivated; 4,300,000 acres are undeveloped. Thus we see that the drainage enterprises which have been organized to drain wet lands contain a large acreage that is, at present, only partly reclaimed. Some of this is once-reclaimed land that is now wet land because of poorly constructed or poorly operated drainage works.

In this compilation of drainable wet lands in organized drainage enterprises, the first ten states in acreage of wet drainable lands are, in order of their importance: Michigan, Minnesota, Arkansas, Indiana, Ohio, Iowa, Illinois, Mississippi, Texas, and Louisiana. Michigan has 3,600,000 acres, and the next four states have over 3,000,000 acres each. Louisiana, with the smallest acreage, has about 1,300,000 acres.

The second compilation, listing the wet drainable lands not in organized drainage enterprises, shows a total of approximately 20,100,000 acres. This compilation, titled "Acreage of Fertile Wet Land Outside of Drainage Enterprises That Can Be Provided With Community Outlet Drainage at Reasonable Cost," shows a total of 13,700,000 acres of undeveloped land and 6,-400,000 acres of partially farmed land. In this compilation, the first ten states are, in order of acreages: Louisiana, Texas, Georgia, North Carolina, Mississippi, Alabama, Arkansas, Minnesota, and Virginia. For each of the first six of these states the acreage is above 1,000,000. Virginia, tenth in order, contains 700,000 acres.

One contention, based on sound reasoning, is that if we are to invest public funds in federal reclamation work, we will get more agricultural production for the same investment from drainage reclamation than from irrigation reclamation. There is, however, a feature of the present large Western reclamation projects which cannot be ignored in this comparison. That feature is power. Power development is committed to repay $1,020,-000 of the $1,372,000,000 total federal investment in federal reclamation projects. Some $546,000,000 of this is power investment and $474,000,000 is payment by power on the investment in irrigation development. Furthermore, the power of the Western reclamation projects aids our national industrial expansion and dispersion.

As far as we now know, we shall not soon have need for the expansion of agricultural production that could be had from a large federal program of drainage reclamation. For some of these wet lands, a public program of engineering works, comparable with Western irrigation reclamation, would be required. But such a program would not fit the major part of the total acreage. Many of the present drainage enterprises need mainly good engineering advice and technical leadership, and better state legislation and administration to facilitate drainage-district organization and operation. According to those who are currently studying this problem, only one of the states most concerned with agricultural land drainage has an active state organization working with federal agencies on drainage. That state is Louisiana.[1]

Probably a federal program for federal and federal-state work on agricultural land drainage is now in process of incubation. When such program is developed, the first efforts should

[1] Robert W. Harrison, "Land Economic Research in the Alluvial Valley of the Lower Mississippi," *The Journal of Farm Economics*, August, 1947.

be to provide the technical service and to obtain the state legislation that will help the present organized drainage enterprises to function.

A National Program for Drainage Reclamation

In view of the important part that the drainage reclamation of wet lands has played and will play in the development of our agricultural resources, it seems that we should attempt to envision national policy and a possible national program for the future of this development. What may be the need for such a program? What kind of program, if needed, will serve best? How could federal and state legislation and operations complement each other most effectively in such a program?

As we see from the materials in the preceding pages, there are some 29,000,000 acres of land in organized drainage enterprises, and 24,700,000 acres of this is developed or partially developed land on which the drainage works need rehabilitation or improvement. An additional 4,300,000 acres in this total need drainage in order to be used agriculturally. In addition to this 29,000,000 acres of land in drainage enterprises, there are some twenty million acres of drainable wet lands not now in drainage enterprises, and these lands require some type of drainage work for successful agricultural use.

In the organized drainage enterprises, which have done much of the drainage reclamation, drainage districts are the most usual form of organization. These organizations are formed under state legislative enactments which confer some local governmental powers upon the district. The drainage district has, or may have, taxing and regulatory powers for carrying out its purposes, as well as power to borrow money on mortgage in financing the construction and operation of drainage works.

Many of these drainage enterprises are too small for good natural-area drainage, their operations conflict with those of

189

adjacent districts, and their engineering and operation planning has been faulty. Consolidation of districts and re-engineering of their works are needed to remedy these conflicts and defects. Some of the problems of the interrelationships of the drainage operations extend across state boundaries and are further complicated by differences in state legislation and policy concerning organized drainage enterprises. Engineering and land-use surveys could help to determine what is needed in the consolidation and works replanning of drainage enterprise. This same type of survey and analysis might aid enterprises organized for new drainage work to attain better geographic-area and engineering planning. It also seems desirable that there be greater adherence to an adapted form for the state legislation and state administration relating to organized drainage enterprises.

It seems fairly clear that there is need of a national program for drainage reclamation. This seems true because of the scope and importance of drainage enterprises in the use of our national agricultural resource, and because of the large number of those enterprises that are confronted with problems which are being solved only slowly, if at all. It also seems clear that there is not much drainage reclamation that cannot and will not be done by private drainage enterprises, given good leadership in planning and technical service and good federal and state legislation and administration. There does not appear to be need for a program of public works for drainage reclamation on a pattern of the present program for irrigation reclamation, with the large multipurpose reservoirs. There may, however, be situations of allied influences and joint planning needs between drainage and flood control—situations where the lowest-cost form of flood control would be public subsidy to drainage enterprises for certain construction features which would be beyond the economics of the drainage enterprise.

A federal program of drainage reclamation should, then, be set up essentially as an agricultural engineering and land-use service program, with emphasis on drainage-enterprise surveys

190

and plans, engineering technical service, and state legislative analysis and aid. This program should be able to plan, under reasonably uniform state legislation and administration, the areal and operating interrelationships of drainage enterprises throughout the entire length of a drainage basin. Such a program should be able to give leadership, also, in the relationship of the drainage enterprises to public programs for flood control.

The agency to administer such a drainage reclamation program should be in the Department of Agriculture. On its staff should be engineers trained and experienced in land-use practices; soils technicians who would avert such debacles as some of the drainage reclamation in the Florida Everglades; farm-management technicians who see the interrelationships of drainage-enterprise planning and farm planning; and legislative analysts to aid in a pattern of adapted state legislation. This program must be administered by those who comprehend its relationships with the programs for flood control, wildlife management, and others.

Probably this program would never need to be a large one. Its emphasis would be on information, service, and leadership.

191

IX. Alternatives in River-Basin Development

AREAS OF POLICY IN RIVER-BASIN DEVELOPMENT

Let us state the two extreme points of view regarding the principles which should be followed in the planning and administration of the public development of the water resources of a river basin.

One of these extremes would have this development done and administered in accord with the best possible compromise among local self-interest groups—irrigationists, sportsmen, and power generators—throughout the region. At the other extreme is the view that river-basin development must be centralized in a federal government agency or association of agencies that would be guided primarily by national policy and program design. Neither of these extremes is desirable. By the first, we should lose too much of the regional view and motivation in the public interest; by the second, we should lose adaptation to local conditions. Is there a workable method for integrating the federal, state, and local public and private interest in the development and use of the water resources of a river basin?

It will, perhaps, be helpful to us in seeking the answer to this question, to attempt to define the national, state, and local "areas of policy" in a program for development and use of the water resources of a river basin. Probably such policy areas cannot be definitely segmented, but we should attempt to delineate them, as far as possible. In so doing, we should bear in mind that national policy must have a vision greater than that which will come from a merging and assimilation of local policy, and that local policy must make many adaptations and variations in using and applying a national program.

If we start, then, with a definition of the area of national

192

policy, we try first to see the large boundaries of national public interest in the alternatives for development and use of the water resources of a river basin or other natural region. Entering into this concept of national public interest are the issues of health and safety, of regional rates of economic growth, of military security, and of the balancing of costs with gains, both for the alternatives within the region and between regions. Decisions on these issues must determine the place of flood control, sanitation, public power, navigation, and recreation, and the extent of national public investment, in the development of a river basin or other natural region.

The area of state policy serves as a merging area for the national-policy area, public interest, and the local-policy area, primarily private interest. Thus the area of state policy is, or should be, a key area. It should be recognized as such and should function effectively in the formulation of the national public-interest policy and in the development and adaptation of local self-interest policy. Thus, the area of state policy is that of interpretation and communication between "grass-roots" policy and national policy in the planning and the development of a region's water resource.

Inevitably and necessarily, the area of local policy will concern mainly the local individual and group self-interest in the plans and programs for river-basin development, especially as those programs concern irrigation, power, and recreation. It is eminently desirable that this area of policy have the fullest expression possible within the limits of reason and moderation. From such an expression must come many of the facets of the regional program. Without such an expression, the program cannot fit well and may be a total misfit for the local and regional economy. In the area of local policy, there will be many conflicts of economic interest. These should be resolved, insofar as possible, in the area of state policy, just as conflicts of regional economic interest must, to the fullest degree possible, be reconciled in the area of national policy.

193

Valley Authorities

Most people agree that we should have some form
of organization for basin-wide planning and for unification of
public-affairs programs in the development of the land and water
resources of the main river basins. But they do not agree on the
form that such organization should take. About the only alternative to some such organization is the planning and administration
of public development by and for local self-interest groups, with
little if any administration in the general public interest.

What are the different forms which organization might take
in this field of public affairs? The "valley authority," or federal-
ly-created public corporate entity, is one. We see it at work in
the Tennessee Valley. Another form now in operation is a formal-
ized operating program provided through legislation and appropriations for the federal bureaus most concerned in the development program. We see this now in the work of the Bureau of
Reclamation and the Army Corps of Engineers for the Missouri
Valley. A federal-state Missouri Basin Interagency Committee
has been organized to help co-ordinate the program for these
federal agencies in their Missouri Valley program.

Another form of river-basin organization may be the planning and program-forming that center around an interstate
compact for development and use of the water and the power
of a river. We see some semblance of this in the Colorado River
Compact, which defines the functions of federal agencies—such
as the Bureau of Reclamation, the Corps of Engineers, and the
Federal Power Administration—in the management of reservoirs
constructed under the provisions of federal and state legislation
growing out of the compact. For example, the Boulder Canyon
Dam Act, under which the Hoover Dam was constructed, dedi-
cates one block of the Mead Lake storage to irrigation, one block
to power, and one block to flood control. Thus is defined and
limited the management of each of several operating agencies.
The Colorado River Compact is the vehicle for the Boulder Canyon Dam Act and for certain related state legislation.

194

Yet another possible form of river basin organization might be a set of federal and state enabling acts, for the states of the basin, to create a federal-state board which would be the official group to plan the development and sponsor the legislation. Under such legislation, the federal and state operation agencies would function within their respective bounds as defined by the legislation. No such organization has as yet been attempted.

Few will argue that the valley authority has not served the public interest well in the Tennessee Valley. Yet many do question whether this type of organization fits the Western river basins. Reasons given for this doubt are the multitude of Western private water rights and values, the conflicts of those rights with power in the storage and delivery of limited water resources, and the need for careful local consideration of the several possible kinds of water developments and their uses. T.V.A. administration has admittedly been close to the local communities and problems. But, say some of the critics of this form of organization, that is just fortuitous and probably would not happen again. Perhaps one Western valley authority should be tried out to see whether it does fit and will work. How else, it may be argued, can we know?

Concerning the type of river-basin organization that we have in the present Missouri Valley development program, it is said by some to be a hastily conceived program advocated by certain federal agencies to forestall other possible federal development programs for the region. It does seem possible that the present program for the Missouri Valley is too narrow, is not well matured, and has had too much and too rapid "bureau planning." If this is true, there could be great and far-reaching mistakes that would warp the economy of the regions or cause the tremendous investments required to yield only limited benefit. So far, the discussions and recommendations of the Interagency Committee seem to have been contained too much within the present program.

195

A river-basin interstate compact is not, it seems fair to say, a form of organization for river-basin planning and development. Although it may do so in the future, it has not yet served as a vehicle for such organization. We may say this because we do not yet have for the Colorado River any plan of river development; and we have not had, in the twenty-five or more years of duration of the Colorado River Compact, the growth and definition of that compact that is needed for such a river-basin plan. It does seem that the growth and refinement of the original concept could have taken place—perhaps yet can occur—and that consequently this compact might serve as the means for agreement upon a basin-wide plan for the development and use of the Colorado River resource. But, instead of this, we have a stalemate and mutterings of an impending contest. The compact as a vehicle for organization may become discredited.

For the fourth of our possible alternatives for river-basin planning and development, here is a proposed pattern:

(1) A federal enabling act to create a federal-state river-basin commission for the basin, which would develop a program and sponsor the legislation to implement that program. This act would define, as far as practicable, the spheres of federal and state agencies in carrying out the program that is developed.

(2) Parallel legislation by the states, for defining the make-up and functions of the commissions.

(3) The work of program development by the commission and the sponsoring of legislation to implement that program.

(4) The carrying out of the development work and of the program administration by the state and federal action agencies within their functions as defined by the enabling acts and the subsequent program legislation.

Perhaps some may say that such a program for joint federal-state action is unrealistic.

Can they propose a more workable plan?

196

The cause—denuded "sore spots" high on the mountain ridges

The effect—flood-devastated towns and farm lands

THE SANTA FÉ "AGREEMENT"

ON NOVEMBER 4, 1922, the Colorado River Interstate Water Compact, sometimes referred to as the "Santa Fé Agreement," was signed at Santa Fé, New Mexico, by the Colorado River Basin Commission. This commission consisted of one representative from each of the seven states of the basin and one federal representative. Consent for this interstate compact to apportion the waters of the Colorado River was provided in an Act of Congress of August 19, 1921.[1] This compact was ratified during the year 1923 by all of the seven states except Arizona.

Let us review this compact and the related subsequent events primarily with a view to answering this question: Can the interstate river-basin compact provide the vehicle for the development and management of the water resources of a river basin?

The compact that was signed at Santa Fé can and should be regarded as the initial phase of a concept and of an implement that were intended to evolve and grow through continuous negotiation and definition. Viewed in this light, the compact looks good, even though the agreed-on features of the compact were limited and sometimes obscure. In this compact and in the subsequent Boulder Canyon Project Act, there are contained the needed precedents and provisions for further negotiation and growth of the agreement concerning the apportionment and uses of the water resources of the river. Such growth of the agreement is essential for the construction and development programs for storing and managing the river's water resources.

In its studies of the Colorado River, the commission which signed the compact at Santa Fé concluded that the river had sufficient resources to divide an average annual flow of 15,000,-000 acre-feet equally between the upper-basin states—Wyoming, Colorado, Utah, and New Mexico—and the lower-basin states of Arizona, California, and Nevada. This division of the

[1] 42 *Stat.*, 171.

197

water for "beneficial consumptive use" was made between the upper and lower basins, and the lower basin was given the right to increase its use above the 7,500,000 acre-feet by an additional 1,000,000 acre-feet annually. The compact also provides for granting a share of the Colorado River water to Mexico. This share is to come out of surplus—presumably above the 16,000,-000 acre-feet apportioned—and if the surplus proves insufficient, the deficiency is to be borne equally between the upper and lower basins of the river. The compact further provides for division of unallotted water after 1963, and sets up the procedure for negotiation of this division and for negotiation between the states to settle claims concerning division of water to the individual states.

Thus we see that the compact did not make a final distribution of shares of the water to the states of the basin. It does divide the water between the upper and lower basins, and it provides the method for continued negotiation and agreement as to final allotment to each of the states. The growth of this very important feature of the compact depends upon the continued activity of the first agreement.

Studies of the water resources of the Colorado concluded since the compact was signed in 1922 fix the probable average annual "virgin flow" of the river, where it enters Mexico, at 17,720,000 acre-feet. This figure, based on the series of years 1897–1943, covers the measured flow at the boundary and the estimated upstream diversions for irrigation and other consumptive uses. It is estimated that this "virgin flow" of the river at the international boundary has varied from a low of 5,000,000 acre-feet to a high of 25,000,000 acre-feet.

As a condition for the support of the Boulder Canyon Project Act by the six other Colorado-basin states, California enacted legislation limiting her share of Colorado water to 4,400,000 acre-feet annually. Then the Boulder Canyon Act passed in 1928 authorizes the three lower-basin states to enter into agreement apportioning the 7,500,000 acre-feet allotted to the lower basin as follows: California 4,400,000 acre-feet, Arizona 2,800,000 acre-feet, and Nevada 300,000 acre-feet. This act further provides that California shall receive, in addition, one-half of the surplus waters unapportioned by the compact. A similar provision is made in the Boulder Canyon Project Act for Arizona. The act of 1928 thus provides some definitions and perhaps some modifications of the compact. Probably these definitions were essential for the success of the Boulder Canyon Project Act. It seems that they should have grown out of a continuation of activity and negotiation under the compact.

As provided for by the Colorado River Compact, a treaty with Mexico, concluded in 1945, granted 1,500,000 acre-feet of Colorado River water to that nation. California representatives opposed this treaty on the grounds that the amount of the grant was unnecessarily large. Arizona did not oppose the treaty, but insists that the waters of the Gila are exempt from any more than a proportional allotment to Mexico under the treaty. Arizona claims that the provision of Section B of Article III of the compact, granting an added 1,000,000 acre-feet, above the 7,500,000, to the lower basin, applies specifically to the Gila, for Arizona. Arizona insists, then, that the 2,800,000 acre-feet granted in the Boulder Canyon Project Act is her share of the water from Mead Lake and that the Gila water is additional to this. She ratified the Colorado River Compact in 1944, only after receiving a contract from the Secretary of the Interior for an annual right, subject to the provisions of the Colorado River Compact, for 2,800,000 acre-feet from Lake Mead.

Now let us total the claims on the waters of the river. California has the 4,400,000 acre-feet, and her representatives claim another 962,000 acre-feet as her share of the surplus water unallotted by the compact. This claim of share of surplus would throw all of the burden of the Mexican treaty grant upon the other states. This figure of 926,000 can be derived approximately by labeling the difference between the 17,720,000 acre-feet average flow and the 15,000,000 acre-feet apportionment—or

2,720,000—as surplus. From this would be subtracted the estimated annual evaporation loss of 800,000 acre-feet from the Colorado River reservoirs. Then one-half of the difference between 2,720,000 and 800,000, or 1,920,000, equals 960,000. The table below shows the claims on the water resources of the Colorado River.

California	4,400,000
" (surplus)	962,000
Arizona (Mead Lake)	2,800,000
" (Gila River)	1,000,000
Nevada	300,000
Mexican treaty	1,500,000
Reservoir evaporation	800,000
Lower-basin total	11,762,000
Upper-basin states	7,500,000
River total	19,262,000

These claims total approximately 1,500,000 acre-feet more than the 17,720,000 acre-feet estimated as the resources of the river. This estimate seems to be high rather than low.

Approximately half of the water resources of the Colorado are now in actual use, with the larger part of this use in the lower-basin states. Arizona's main use of Mead Lake water depends upon construction of the Central Arizona Project, which would take about 1,000,000 acre-feet annually from Mead Lake into Gila drainage by a 900-foot pump lift. California's Imperial Valley irrigation use is now about 2,700,000 acre-feet, but this is nearly 1,000,000 acre-feet more than actually necessary. This unneeded water now wastes into Salton Sea. Needed use of Colorado River water by the Los Angeles area may expand greatly.

Thus, instead of continued negotiation for growth of the compact signed at Santa Fé on November 4, 1922, there now seems to be shaping up between the compact states the "Battle for the River." The argument fumes in a multiplicity of claims and counterclaims, some of them obviously ill-considered.

It is now proposed by representatives of certain of the lower-basin states to seek recourse in litigation to determine the intents and consequences of the compact instead of undertaking renewed negotiation by a commission to attain the needed growth of the original compact concepts. If litigation does prove to be the necessary recourse in this case, it does not augur well for future use of the interstate compact as a basis for planning, developing, and managing the water resources of a river basin. But there are alternatives other than the interstate compact.

X. Conclusion

POLICY ISSUES AND ALTERNATIVES

Public policies and public affairs concerning land and water use have many important influences upon Western economy, more so than in the other regions of the nation. Nevertheless, the policy issues in Western land and water are not essentially different from those of the other regions of the United States, and must be thought of in national rather than in regional terms. Programs designed to implement national land- and water-use policies need special Western regional and local adaptations.

To a degree seldom fully realized, the Western parts of the United States are yet a frontier in many aspects of land and water use. We yet have to find the key to best uses and stability for much of the land and water resource of the arid West. National policy in the development of Western land and water resources should aim at a better balance in our Western population and economy—should aim at increasing the economic opportunity in those regions and areas that have an unfavorable relative growth and development rate. Western land and water resources can strengthen and enrich our national economy far more than they now do. That result will depend, to a large extent, upon the special applications and effectiveness of land- and water-use policies and programs in the Western regions.

We have some special problems of land-resource conservation in the West, problems that could be disbelieved and disregarded until it is too late. Nature must do much of the healing of misused Western lands, and nature's healing efforts are less tenacious in arid regions. Our main Western conservation-policy issues concern those submarginal and destructive types of dry-

202

land farming, the losses in the range-plant and soil resources through overuse and unadapted use, and the deterioration of watershed lands and consequent sedimentation. Much of the corrective action must come through public programs for land and water use, in recognition of the public interest in a resource-conservation problem that is now beyond the scope and the means of the farms and ranches that use the land.

Permanent federal public ownership of the Western lands now in such ownership is yet an open question of policy for certain types of land. This question is probably closed for the lands that have important watershed, forestry, and recreation values. In the development of policy regarding future public or private ownership of the lands of the public domain, careful consideration should be given to their public values and their conservation needs in the public interest. For the public lands of the West that are clearly multiple-use lands—and most of them are—we face an important policy question of management flexibility in the making of adjustments among the uses and the interests, including the general public interest, of the users. The grazing use of the public lands, for example, probably cannot be given better tenure than now prevails, without possible jeopardy of the other uses and the greater values of the lands.

Range livestock grazing is and will continue to be an important use of Western lands, and an important segment of Western economy. However, the Western range is and for some time has been a declining resource. We face the question of how to change this trend while yet using the resource. Perhaps, before it is too late, we can gain through management an up trend on much of the Western range resource. Some of it seems destined to slip rapidly below the margin of economic use.

Federal reclamation is now closely associated with the development of hydroelectric power. Such power has, in fact, become the key to most of the present federal reclamation development. Here the issue is not alone one of the expansion of Western irrigation agriculture. Important questions of population distribution and of Western industrial development and location are implied. Because of the scope of our present water-resource development projects and programs, we should have much more public interest, debate, and participation in the planning of the programs and projects. We should probably give more attention to those public aids that would help private reclamation expansion, recognizing that such expansion applies best to those situations and conditions where the public-interest features of the development are minor rather than major considerations.

Most important of the forestry issues which we face is what kind of forestry programs or integration of programs can improve the future production of private forestry. Most of our future production and supplies must come from that source. Our present reserves of timber on the federal public lands will probably serve as a cushion in a transition to more productive private forestry. Meanwhile, we may need to expand public forest ownership, both federal and state, in order to increase forest production and conserve forest-land resource, and also to enhance the recreational, wildlife, and watershed values of some cutover and burned-over lands where forest regeneration and growth are slow.

Land-use measures for flood control on the private lands upstream are as yet minor in flood-control programs. As we attain better understanding of upstream land use in downstream flood control, we may place considerably more emphasis on land use and much less on river engineering. There appear to be important but as yet undeveloped interrelationships between the drainage reclamation of wet lands and other drainage, and the work of flood control downstream. Thus it seems more and more apparent that the control, development, and use of the water resources of a major drainage basin should be accomplished through basin-wide plans and programs.

In such development of the water resources of a river basin, choice must be made regarding the type of organization best suited as the vehicle for the development and operation. The organization might be a valley authority, on the T.V.A. pattern; a co-operative organization of several agencies or bureaus; a grouping of agencies around an interstate compact and related legislation; or some formal plan of federal and state organization, legislation, and operations. We need to gain more understanding of the potentialities and suitability of these different kinds of organization for the development and use of the water resources of different regions and river basins.

LINES OF ACTION

PROGRAMS to carry out land- and water-use policies embody one or more of four lines of action: (1) educational work, (2) public-private co-operation, (3) administrative action, and (4) regulative action. We have a great deal to learn about how these different lines of action fit best into different kinds of programs and about the supplementary and complementary relationships of these lines of action.

Educational work as a line of action is typified by the work of the federal and state agricultural extension services. Principally, this line of action applies to progress in farm and ranch practices and in management that will lower costs and increase income for the farm and ranch operator. Usually, the changes must be within the scope of the individual operator or of small groups of operators. This line of action does not apply well to those land- and water-use programs that require individual sacrifice in the public interest.

Public-private co-operation as a line of action usually involves benefit payments from a public agency to individuals— land owners or users—to induce actions designed primarily to attain objectives in the general public interest and welfare. There may be secondary and future objectives of financial gain to the co-operator, and on this basis the co-operator may share part of the cost of the program. This line of action is typified by the work of the Soil Conservation Service, in which the cost of soil

205

conservation may be shared in some relationship by the public agency and the co-operator. Another illustration of this type of action is the aids extended to private forestry through the Norris-Doxey and the Clark-McNary programs. Necessarily, educational work supplements the co-operative features of these programs. If and when the changes induced through a program of co-operative work are found to be remunerative to the private co-operator, co-operative action should yield to educational work as the line of action.

Administrative action may be described as government enterprise to accomplish program objectives in the public interest, or to accomplish resource development beyond the scope and risk-bearing capacity of private enterprise. Illustrations of such enterprise are federal reclamation, flood control installations, and the operation of the national forests. Usually, though not universally, the outlet for the tangible production of the government enterprise is the local private business enterprise—such as farms, power distributors, and lumber industries. In this relationship between the public enterprise and the private enterprise, education may well supplement administration.

Regulation of the uses of privately owned land and water resources is a line of action not much used. Its use is limited mainly to those objectives concerning the general public welfare. Sometimes the purpose is protection of the members of a community against financial loss due to the action of some of those in the community. Illustrations of this are prescribed dry-land tillage practices to control soil drifting, and regulation of the number and spacing of wells for draft on a ground-water resource. An illustration of a regulatory action for purposes somewhat more in the general public interest is the zoning of rural lands against farm settlement and arable agriculture. This kind of action must work through the powers of the state government to police the uses of private resources in the public interest. It is apparent, then, that use of this type of action in a federal government program must depend upon suitable state legislation.

Why, it may be asked, must we have regulatory action if we have adequate educational work in land and water use? The answer is that there always may be those who would jeopardize public or community interest for the prospect of a greater immediate gain to themselves. We shall probably see increased use of this type of action.

These distinctions that we have drawn in these four lines of action may seem somewhat artificial. All of them may blend in varying degrees in some land- and water-use programs. Nevertheless, we can better understand the organization and operation of such programs if we differentiate these lines of action and think of their special applications and interrelationships in program design and operation.

Bibliography

I. WESTERN LAND RESOURCES AND THE
NATIONAL ECONOMY

Rasmussen, D. I. "Biotic communities of the Haibab Plateau, Arizona," *Ecological Monographs,* Vol. III (July, 1941), 299–375.

Saunderson, Mont H. "Cattle Production and Marketing in the West," *The American Cattle Producer,* Vol. XXIII, No. 10 (March, 1942).

———. "Ranch Country," *The American Cattle Producer,* Vol. XXVIII, No. 2 (July, 1946).

———. "Some Economic Aspects of the Upland Watershed Lands of the Western United States," *The Journal of Land and Public Utility Economics,* Vol. XV (1939), 480–82.

Stoddart, L. A. and D. I. Rasmussen. *Deer Management and Range Livestock Production. Circular No. 121,* Utah Agricultural Experiment Station, Logan, Utah. June, 1945.

Tennessee Valley Authority. *Food at the Grass Roots—The Nation's Stake in Soil Minerals.* Knoxville, Tennessee, 1947.

U. S. Congress. *Seminar Hearings* before the Subcommittee of the House of Representatives on Irrigation and Reclamation. 80 Cong., 1 sess. February, 1947.

U. S. Department of Agriculture. Forest Service. *Basic Forest Statistics of the U. S., as of Beginning of 1945.* July, 1946.

———. *Forest Outings.* 1940.

———. *Forests and the Nation's Water Resource. Report* of the chief of the U. S. Forest Service. 1947.

———. "Gaging the Timber Resource of the United States." *Report No. 1* from *A Reappraisal of the Forest Situation.* 1946.

———. "The Management Status of Forest Lands in the U. S." *Report No. 3* from *A Reappraisal of the Forest Situation.* 1946.

———. *Some Plain Facts about the Forests. Miscellaneous Publication No. 543.* April, 1944.

———. *Timber Shortage or Timber Abundance. Report* of the chief of the U. S. Forest Service. 1946.

U. S. Department of the Interior. Fish and Wildlife Service. *Big Game Resources of the United States, 1937–1942. Research Report No. 8.* 1944.

Wycoff, Stephen M. "California's Watersheds," *The Journal of Forestry,* Vol. XLVI, No. 2 (February, 1948).

II. The West Faces a Conservation Debacle

Adams, Frank, Paul Ewing, and M. R. Huberty. *Hydrologic Aspects of Burning Brush and Woodland-Grass Ranges in California.* California Department of Natural Resources, Sacramento, California. January, 1947.

Cottam, Walter P. *Is Utah Sahara Bound? Bulletin No. 11,* University of Utah, Salt Lake City. February, 1947.

Kellogg, Charles E. *The Soils That Support Us.* New York, The Macmillan Company, 1941.

Morris, Earl H. *Archeological Studies in the LaPlata District, Southwestern Colorado and Northeastern New Mexico.* Washington, D. C., The Carnegie Institution, 1939.

Sampson, Arthur W. *Plant Succession on Burned Chapparal Lands in Northern California. Bulletin No. 685,* University of California, College of Agriculture, Agricultural Experiment Station, Berkeley, California. March, 1944.

Saunderson, Mont H. "Some Economic Aspects of the Conservation of Western Grazing Lands," *Annals of the Montana Academy of Science,* October, 1941.

Shantz, H. L. *Fire as a Tool in Management of Brush Ranges.* California Department of Natural Resources, Sacramento, California. January, 1947.

U. S. Congress. *Hearings* before the Subcommittee on Public Lands of the Committee on Public Lands, House of Representatives. 80 Cong., 1 sess., *Committee Hearings No. 22* and *23.* September, 1947.

U. S. Department of Agriculture. Forest Service. *Water and Our Forests. Miscellaneous Publication No. 600.* March, 1946.

III. Some National Aspects of Western Land Policy

American Farm Bureau Federation. *A Handbook of Materials Relating to Land and Water Use.* Mimeographed. Chicago, 1947.

Fenneman, Nevin M. *Physiography of the Western United States.* New York, McGraw-Hill Book Company, 1931.

Hibbard, B. H. *A History of Public Land Policies.* New York, The Macmillan Company, 1939.

Saunderson, Mont H. "The National Forest Officer Looks at Resource Values," *The Journal of Forestry,* Vol. XLV, No. 4 (April, 1947).

———. "Relationship between Productivity and Assessed Value of Range Lands," *Proceedings* of the 1948 Annual Conference of the National Tax Association.

U. S. Congress. *Agriculture Looks Ahead.* 80 Cong., 2 sess., *Report* of the House of Representatives Committee on Agriculture. March, 1948.

———. *Tax Problems Connected with Federal Public Lands* (Union Calendar No. 610). 78 Cong., 2 sess., House of Representatives *Report No. 1884.*

———. *The Western Range.* 74 Cong., 2 sess., *Sen. Doc. 199.* 1936.

U. S. Department of Agriculture. *State Legislation for Better Land Use.* A special report by a U.S.D.A. interbureau committee. April, 1941.

U. S. Department of Agriculture and U. S. Department of Commerce. *Graphic Summary of Land Use in the U. S.* 1947.

U. S. Department of the Interior. Bureau of Reclamation. *Reclamation Handbook.* 1942.

IV. Western Public Lands: What and Why They Are

Saunderson, Mont H. "Western Stock Ranch Earnings and Values," *The American Cattle Producer,* Vol. XXVII, No. 7 (December, 1945).

U. S. Congress. *Federal Contributions to States and Local Governmental Units with Respect to Federally Owned Real Estate.* 78 Cong., 1 sess., *House Doc. 216.* 1943.

U. S. Department of Agriculture. Bureau of Agricultural Economics. *Acquisition and Use of Land for Military and War Production Purposes—World War II. War Records Monograph 5.* August, 1947.

———. *Federal Rural Lands.* June, 1947.

V. Livestock Grazing and Land Use

The Record Stockman, 1948 Annual Edition—59th year, No. 1 (January, 1948).

The Western Farm Life, 1948 Annual Herdsman Edition, Vol. L, No. 1 (January, 1948).

VI. Reclamation, Whither Bound?

Joss, Alexander. "Repayment Experience on Federal Reclamation Projects." *Proceedings* of the Annual Conference of the Western Farm Economics Association. 1944.

U. S. Congress. *Hearings* before the House of Representatives Committee on Irrigation and Reclamation on *H.R. 520,* "Settlement of Returning Veterans on Farms in Reclamation Projects." Parts I and II, 1945.

————. *Hearings* before the House of Representatives Subcommittee on Irrigation and Reclamation on Proposed Amendments to the Reclamation Act of 1939. 80 Cong., 1 sess., *Committee Hearing No. 4.* April, 1947.

————. *Hearings* before the Senate Irrigation and Reclamation Subcommittee *on S. 912,* a bill exempting certain projects from the land limitation provisions of federal reclamation laws. 80 Cong., 1 sess. May and June, 1947.

U. S. Department of the Interior. Bureau of Reclamation. *Land Ownership Survey on Reclamation Projects.* 1946.

————. *Project Repayment Histories and Payout Schedules.* January, 1947.

Weeks, David. *American Irrigation Policies.* New York, American Council, Institute of Pacific Relations, 1933.

VII. Transition in Forestry

American Forestry Association. *Proceedings,* the American Forestry Congress, Washington, D. C. 1946.

Gillett, Charles A. "Aids to Farm Forestry." *Proceedings,* the Annual Conference of the Society of American Foresters. 1947.

Johnson, Neil W. "Wartime Experience in Production Adjustment Research, and Some Future Possibilities," *The Journal of Farm Economics,* Vol. XXVII, No. 4 (November, 1945).

McArdle, R. E. "Technical Assistance to Private Forest Owners," *The Journal of Forestry*, Vol. XLV, No. 1 (January, 1947).

U. S. Congress. *A National Plan for American Forestry.* 2 vols. 73 Cong., 1 sess., *Sen Doc. 12.* 1933.

U. S. Department of Agriculture. Forest Service. *The Work of the U. S. Forest Service. Miscellaneous Publication No. 290.* 1945.

VIII. Flood-Control and Drainage Programs and Policies

North Carolina State College Agricultural Experiment Station and the Tennessee Valley Authority, co-operating. *Land Cover in Relation to Water Control and Utilization in the Upper French Broad River Watershed.* Agricultural Experiment Station *Bulletin No. 339.* June, 1943.

Phillips, George R. "The Flood Control Program of the U. S. Department of Agriculture," *The Journal of Forestry*, Vol. XLV, No. 10 (October, 1947).

U. S. Department of Agriculture. Forest Service. *Grazing and Floods.* Forest Service *Bulletin 91.* September 15, 1911.

IX. Alternatives in River-Basin Development

Tennessee Valley Authority. *Annual Report* of the T.V.A. for 1945. Knoxville, Tennessee.

———. *A Study of the Work of the Land Grant Colleges in the Tennessee Valley Area in Co-operation with the T. V. A.* 1939.

U. S. Congress. *Hearings* before the House of Representatives Subcommittee on Irrigation and Reclamation on *H.R. 5434*, a bill reauthorizing the Gila Federal Reclamation Project and containing other measures. Parts I and II, 1946.

U. S. Department of Agriculture. Bureau of Agricultural Economics. *Agricultural Development Problems of the Missouri Valley.* A presentation by the B.A.E. before the Senate Committee on Irrigation and Reclamation. September, 1945.

U. S. Department of Agriculture. Farm Credit Administration. "Remodeling the Missouri River Basin," *The Farm Credit Leader* (publication of the Farm Credit Administration office of Omaha, Nebraska), 1948 Spring Issue.

U. S. Department of the Interior. Bureau of Reclamation. *The Colorado River.* A departmental report. March, 1946.

212

Index

Western Land and Water Use

HAS BEEN SET ON THE LINOTYPE

IN ELEVEN POINT OLD STYLE

NUMBER SEVEN, WITH TWO

POINTS BETWEEN LINES

AND PRINTED ON ANTIQUE PAPER

UNIVERSITY OF OKLAHOMA PRESS

NORMAN